5-21-69

SPEECH ORIGINS AND DEVELOPMENT

Speech as the involuntary accompaniment of "Bodily Effort."

SPEECH ORIGINS AND DEVELOPMENT

By

EDMUND CRITCHLEY, M.A., B.M., M.R.C.P.

Research Fellow and Lecturer in Neurology
University of Kentucky Medical Center
Lexington, Kentucky

CHARLES C THOMAS · PUBLISHER
Springfield · Illinois · U.S.A.

Published and Distributed Throughout the World by

CHARLES C THOMAS • PUBLISHER

BANNERSTONE HOUSE

301-327 East Lawrence Avenue, Springfield, Illinois, U.S.A.

NATCHEZ PLANTATION HOUSE

735 North Atlantic Boulevard, Fort Lauderdale, Florida, U.S.A.

With THOMAS BOOKS careful attention is given to all details of manufacturing and design. It is the Publisher's desire to present books that are satisfactory as to their physical qualities and artistic possibilities and appropriate for their particular use. THOMAS BOOKS will be true to those laws of quality that assure a good name and good will.

Printed in the United States of America

W-2

1505095

To Mair

PREFACE

T HE PURPOSE OF this book is to present a concept of the origin and development of speech in a form meaningful to those whose chosen specialities impinge on this fascinating subject.

The historical attitudes, exemplified by the belief in a *lingua adamaica*, by the early anthropological hypotheses, and the writings of the Darwinian evolutionists are lightly touched upon. They lead into a discussion of animal communication and an analysis of present-day speech in its literate and popular forms in civilized and primitive communities.

The author's specialized interests are reflected in chapters on the essential requirements for speech, childhood speech, the linguistic aspects of gesture and the methods of communication used by the deaf.

The physiological anatomy of the organs of speech reception and expression is presented in outline and mention made of disordered function of these organs. Childhood speech is reviewed as an organistic whole, very dependent upon a variety of sensory stimuli for the full perfection of its development. Differing patterns of sensory deprivation may be observed in children reared in the wild state, in deaf or blind children, and in those of low intelligence.

The linguistic aspects of gesture are treated at length. It is more usual for these either to be ignored completely or to be discussed to the exclusion of all other hypotheses of speech origins. Three aspects of gesture are discussed for the first time: the ontogenetic development of gestural ability, the role of "muscular memory" in the selection of words, and the difficulty which deaf children experience in understanding abstract terms, in whatever form they may be presented.

The human brain is remarkable. Brain growth continues beyond the perinatal period. There is an asymmetry in the localization of cerebral function, and the cortical cells are linked by an

vii

abundance of interconnections. Man's special talents include the gift of speech, the use of tools and the capacity for abstract thought. In this synthesis we have a dynamic picture of speech evolving in relation to man's conceptual understanding.

This is a very personal book. My training in otolaryngology, pediatrics and neurology has drawn my attention to the very diversity of the problems connected with speech and the need to possess an appreciation of the mechanics of language. The desire to write a book on speech arose during the course of a study of deafness and, in particular, of the social upbringing of hearing children whose parents were severely deaf. My thoughts on the origin of speech first appeared in the form of a lecture to the Spanish Department of Westfield College, University of London. This lecture provided the basis upon which I have written this book.

I wish to thank all those with whom I have had many valuable discussions upon this topic, Charles C Thomas, Publisher for help in the production of this book and Mr. R. Herndon and Mr. G. Courtney of the Medical Illustration Department of the University of Kentucky Medical Center for providing the tables and illustrations.

E. C.

CONTENTS

SPEECH ORIGINS AND DEVELOPMENT

Chapter 1

THE BEGINNINGS

A SUMMARY OF ATTITUDES THROUGH THE AGES

It is said that James I of England wanted to see the experiment tried of bringing up a couple of children without ever hearing the sound of a human voice. He conjectured that they would speak "pure Hebrew."

R. R. GATES
Wolf Children and Feral Man.

THERE IS A power in language, a mystical property, which has perplexed man throughout the ages. He remains in awe of his own ability to speak and use language. He will have read in history, even if he has not experienced in his own life, the remarkable fashion whereby words have changed man's action: Wise words have averted mortal conflict, injudicious words have produced disaster.

Words have never seemed to be earthly. They belong to the spirit or soul, and rest uneasily on the body. They depart with the breath of life. They are man's link with the supernatural. In more regions than not, it has been supposed that language is the direct gift of the immortals to their chosen creation—to mankind at large.

The earlier gods were gruesome. The words they spake were terrifying and mighty. Man was subjugated by language. He faltered when he came to reply. He strove for a greater share of the secret of language, and even today the *mystique* remains; for ability to harness the full power of language for the benefit of mankind eludes us still.

The Greek gods were kinder. They were almost human and shared the gossip, the depravity and the tittle-tattle of humans. But the tradition that language came from the gods continued.

3

In Christendom a similar assumption was held. God made Adam to speak. The first language may therefore be termed the *lingua adamaica*. One may quote the Gospel according to St. John: "In the beginning was the word, and the word was with God, and the word was God. The same was in the beginning with God."

The original language was supposed to be perfect: its successors degenerate. Would Adam have further opportunity to be entrusted with the naming of the animals? "The Lord God formed man of the dust of the ground, and breathed into his nostrils the breath of life; and the breath of life became in man a speaking spirit . . . And whatsoever Adam called every living creature, that was the name thereof."

In the Authorized Version of the Bible the words used are slightly different: "and breathed into his nostrils the breath of life; and man became a living soul;" thereby signifying that of all the animals only man has a soul. But the earlier version is yet more significant for it gives the moment when man came to possess the divine gift of speech. There is no more enthralling scene in the Old Testament than that in the Garden of Eden, when God brought every beast of the field and every fowl of the air before Adam to see what he would call them. Not only does it make emphatic the uniqueness of the gift of speech to man, but here is Adam shown to be positively assisting God in his Grand Design.

"I named them as they passed, and understood their Nature," declares Adam in *Paradise Lost;* and, lest we should fail to grasp the significance, N. J. Jacobs has written an amusing and erudite commentary (*Naming Day in Eden*): "With his invisible breath he devised unheard of names, substantial enough to be freighted with deep thoughts and mobile enough to waft their precious cargo down the ages. God had created the earth, and Adam has festooned it with a web of words. With this second creation man gave the world its first constitution. In language he found a foothold and a lever to move the solid world. The verbal execution of this conception deserves the highest praise because it was the greatest single achievement of the human mind and bears the indispensable marks of genius."

Belief in a *lingua adamaica* is wedded to any literal interpretation of the Bible. There have been eras in our history when a looser interpretation has been permitted; and at these times other theories have flourished. The story of creation as told in Genesis could be challenged and Buffon, Erasmus, Darwin and others could propound theories very similar to Herbert Spenser's evolutionary philosophy. In the lush leniency of the eighteenth century heterodox speculations were tolerated and dissention flourished. Many of these were the fantastic musings of poets or the fairy-tale become folklore. But with the advent of the nineteenth century the orthodox Biblical story of the *lingua adamaica* was upheld tenaciously and less fanatically supported notions withered before it. The historic import of the evolutionary thinking of Darwin and others of that period rests not upon their originality of thought but upon their achievement in gaining universal acceptance against entrenched opinion.

The apotheosis of the *lingua adamaica* by the early Victorians was characteristic of the vigor of the day. They brought a new intensity to all manner of controversy. It was their sincere conviction—as stated by a poet of the time—

> *That life is not an idle ore,*
> *But iron dug from central gloom,*
> *And heated hot with burning fears,*
> *And dipt in baths of hissing tears,*
> *And battered with the shocks of doom,*
> *To shape and use—*

The Bible was interpreted more literally than hitherto since the era of the Puritan Commonwealth. The whole purpose, the *raison d'être* of the world, was to alloy the Christian spirit with the human body. This purpose pervaded everything they did and everything they said. They no longer argued jocularly whether the original language was Hebrew, or Irish, or Hamyritic or Swedish, or Basque, or whether the devil spoke Arabic or French. The *lingua adamaica* is the literal interpretation of the origin of language sanctioned in the Book of Genesis. Alas, Adam was to fall from grace; man was to degenerate and become nearer to the beasts than to God. Adam had known the sum total of the creatures of the earth just as a shepherd would know his flock. And, although another shepherd was to come to restore man's grace in the sight of God, he was to be spurned and man continued in his degeneracy. Through their earnest devotions the Victorians hoped to restore man to his earlier perfection.

Such theories of original perfection in language as the Victorians accepted, and had been accepted by all manner of men under all manner of gods, became untenable when man began to think of an evolution of life—a belief in a chain of being from the simple to the elaborate; "Life's minute beginnings up at last to man." Time-honoured theories allied to man's most fervent aspirations were shattered by the evidence from the "flood" and later from the ice-ages that life could be extinguished. Continents had moved. The fossils in the rocks were seen to represent beings no longer extant on earth. These findings forced people to reappraise theories all but forgotten. There had always been a continuous half-suppressed undercurrent of earlier heresies present in superstition, in folklore, in legend, in older literature and in the bibliographies of the universities. The kindling of the concept of evolution in the minds of men had not occurred with cataclysmic abruptness; it had smouldered in countless minds in the preceding eras only to be overlooked or contemptuously cast aside by the vast majority of people. Aristotle, Leonardo, Montaigne, Descartes and Naudin in their writings had made statements which appear to anticipate Darwin.

There were also more subtle forces at work undermining the foundations of the *lingua adamaica*. A belief in miracles is accepted in both the Old and New Testaments. If God intervenes actively in the lives of men certain happenings can be said to be miraculous. The downfall of a divine theory came in part because man believed in the supernatural. An interpretation of the Biblical Story, which survived mainly in old wives tales, accepted the story of the creation as described in the opening verses of Genesis, but held that when God had completed the creation of the world amid the waters He was left with some creative material, *materia creativandum,* as yet unused. From time to time He would use a little of this material.

Jacobs relates a legend that two animals were created in the

Ark. The pig was formed from the elephant's trunk in order to dispose of the garbage and the cat was sneezed forth by the lion so as to rid the boat of rats. A similar interpretation involving the deity in an act of recreation was placed upon God's gift of speech to man: by divine intervention the dumb-struck Zacharias had his mouth opened, his tongue loosened and he spake and praised God; at Pentecost the spirit of the Holy Ghost enabled the apostles to speak in divers tongues; and, in the land of the plain of Shinar, the confusion of tongues with many new and separate languages descended as a curse upon those who ventured to build the Tower of Babel.

The eclipse of the *lingua adamaica* hypothesis came about because natural phenomenon could be readily explained by Darwinian evolutionary theories. Sir Charles Lyell published the *Principles of Geology*, Malthus his *Essay on Population*, and Charles Darwin his *Origin of Species*. By the weight and detail of his documentation, by his strategic manipulation of the scientific establishment (*fortiter in re suaviter in modo*) and by his ability, despite his infirmity, to fill the patriarchal role in the world of science, Darwin surmounted the opposition of the intelligentsia to the truth of the changing face of nature. This was the foundation of his greatness.

The Darwinians ventured, as if by accident, on to the difficult territory of the origin of man and his speech. Their theories led naturally to a consideration of man's position in relation to the animals. To have shrunk from extending their views to include man would have been tantamount to denial of the veracity of their beliefs. It was reasonable for them to conclude that man "is not the only animal that can make use of language to express what is passing in his mind, and can understand, more or less, what is so expressed by another." For them, human communication had its origins in animal communication.

There were criticisms and such criticisms were to be expected. They were intruders knowing nothing of the science of man and nothing of language. Their reputations were made in the biological and archeological sciences. Their thoroughness of application to these sciences was a byword, their knowledge encyclopedic, their observations exact; but, at the height of their achievement, each evolutionist, almost without exception, was tempted from his minute and factual study of rocks, oceana, flora and fauna, and spent the latter years of his life, with much more dubious evidence at his disposal, few of the skeletons of early man we know today and little accurate knowledge of primitive tribes or their rituals, speculating on the Descent of Man and the Origin of Language. Their work came to lack the conviction which was so apparent in their zoological and botanical writings. At times they were not merely superficial, they were wrong. It is pitiful to read, now that the hoax has been revealed, the numerous books written at the turn of the century and later, analyzing in painstaking detail the probable language of the Piltdown Man. It is astonishing to compare the early training of the Evolutionists and the books which they subsequently wrote. However, those who bring a fresh light to any subject do so through possession of a knowledge or a technique which till then has not been applied to that particular subject. As the combination of knowledge (or technique) and the subject has not previously occurred, the innovators can scarcely be expected to be aware of the minutiae appertaining to the subject: they approach it anew and it is hoped that they possess trained and alert minds with which to grapple with the essentials.

Wherever, as the result of a new proficiency, a new scholarship is brought to bear on a particular problem, and fresh talents and opinions make contact for the first time, the impact is felt on both sides. The innovators will mold afresh the subject and the new experience will mold them. They will begin united in thought. A is obviously incompatible with B. How can opinion B be held any longer? The first essential task for the innovators is to make others, the traditionalists, aware that A is incompatible with B. The traditionalists must suggest a compromise. In practice the first compromise is rarely found to be satisfactory. And then, in order to proceed further, the innovators must learn the subject sufficiently thoroughly to be able to argue on the same level as the traditionalists. Rarely can the innovators advance beyond this stage as a united body of opinion. The rates of adaptation and learning will differ. Different trends will be seen to develop. Some will adhere rigidly to their initial approach, some will espouse the compromise suggested by the traditionalists and others will seek further compromises of their own into which factors C, D, or E may also be blended. The Evolutionists as a body made many contributions to the study of language origins; individual evolutionists made very individual contributions often differing widely from those of their fellows. In time they frequently became highly critical of each other's theories.

Thus many modern biologists who may justly be regarded as the evolutionists of today, notably Eiseley and Darlington, though they adhere to the principles of Natural Selection, are nonetheless highly critical of Darwin's role and have accorded to Wallace an eminence which he did not hold in his own time. Darwin's *Expression of the Emotions in Man and Animals* is no longer regarded as superior to the hypotheses which Wallace adumbrated on speech, and Wallace's contribution on speech has found a new significance. More, too, is known of the theory of prolonged fetalization (pedomorphic development). This theory provides an explanation in keeping with the approach to evolution and natural selection which allows for marked differences between man and the animals. Wallace in his own eccentric way anticipated this development.

Eiseley and Darlington find that Darwin's view of inheritance was "soft," more akin to Lamarck's teleological theory than to the "hard" theories of genetic inheritance later described by Mendel and Weissman. "Soft" inheritance implies that the hereditary matter is malleable and may be affected by environment, whereas "hard" inheritance entails the transmission through successive generations of a germ-plasm isolated from the effects of environment on the body as a whole. Darlington's commentary, *Darwin's Place in History* (1959), draws a sharp contrast between Darwin's original exposition of the theory of evolution and that of Wallace, "although at the time everyone agreed, friends and enemies alike, that this was one theory." Wallace, not Darwin, repudiated Lamarck's hypothesis that environment begets structure. As Darlington comments in acid terms, "He (Darwin) leaves open a line of retreat from caused to directed (selection), the line he was later with unnoticed steps to follow." When the evolutionists turned their attention to man—the significant date is 1860, that of the public discussion between Bishop Wilberforce and Huxley held in Oxford—they relied increasingly upon the studies in comparative anatomy made by Huxley; very little of significance was contributed at firsthand by Darwin. Huxley was obsessed by the closeness of man to the rest of the mammalian sub-kingdom. Huxley was unable to find any anatomical reason to suppose man to be immune from those forces which determined the characteristics and the survival of animals.

In later life Alfred Russel Wallace departed from the position held by Huxley. Wallace was the only member of the inner group of evolutionists to have made a serious anthropological study. During his sojourn in the Malay archipelago he had observed the backward peoples who lived a limited and primitive existence. Their upbringing was truly simple and yet they could readily be trained in tasks outside the requirements of their normal life. He concluded that the linguistic ability of the natives was in no way inferior to that of the higher races. In a prophetic phrase he declared that their brain was "an instrument developed in advance of the needs of its possessor." These people were untrained and unfitted by the processes of selection which had determined their status, nonetheless they were equipped with the potential to adapt themselves to a civilization much higher than their own. He argued that the head size of the Malayan people was not markedly dissimilar to that common among European races. They could thus be expected to possess equal capacity for adaptation to the ways of civilization.

Wallace, the biologist, the rational scientist, somehow equated his belief in evolution with a belief in phrenology, mesmerism and spiritualism: an eccentric combination to say the least. The brainchild of this unlikely combination was his dualist theory of Darwinism as applied to man. It was in part scientific and in part metaphysical. He expanded this theory to include a hypothesis of the origin of speech through gesture. He alone among the early evolutionists emphasized the different nature of the abilities of man and animals, and alone among the evolutionists of his day anticipated the theory of prolonged fetalization.

Wallace argued that Natural Selection depends on the survival of the fittest. For this reason it can only act on useful or hurtful characteristics, eliminating the latter and keeping up the former to a fairly general level of efficiency. It applies, with some approach to equality, among all savages—speed in running, bodily strength, skill with weapons, acuteness of vision, ability to follow a trail. Mathematical, musical or artistic talents—those specially developed faculties of civilized man—exist in only a small proportion of individuals and the difference of capacity between these favored individuals and the average of mankind is enormous. Thus faculties are developed in civilized man which in their mode of origin, their function and their variations are altogether distinct from those other characteristics and faculties which are essential to him, and which have been brought to their actual state of efficiency by the necessities of his existence.

He included speech among man's special talents developed outside the forces of natural selection. Natural selection was inadequate to account for several of the physical as well as the psychical characteristics of man, for example, his soft sensitive skin, his speech, his color sense, and his moral attributes. This was a curious deviation from the orthodox path of the evolutionists for the Darwinians had already recognized sexual selection as important in the operation of the natural selection; the skin, color sense and moral attributes may well be significant sexually. Speech is perhaps not that important in sexual selection but it may well be of great importance in survival.

Chapter 2

EARLY ETYMOLOGICAL HYPOTHESES

All philosophers who find
A favourite system to their mind,
In every point to make it fit
Will force all Nature to submit.

From *Headlong Hall*

T HE EVOLUTIONISTS were not alone in pursuit of the origin of language. The idea of linguistic change aroused insatiable curiosity among other disciplines. Study of language which until then had been regarded with an esthetic pleasure, a proper occupation worthy of any man of breeding and culture, received a new impetus. Those who had previously been content to marvel blissfully at God's supreme gift to man now chose to probe the origin of its creation. They forsook any concern they may have had with Biblical conundrums and sought with Teutonic thoroughness the evolution of language from earlier archaic tongues.

The same worthies still studied language. It still attracted the dilettante and the learned, the classicist, the grammarian, the phonetician, the orientalist, the historian, the comparative philologist, the etymologist and countless other scholars defying description. They tended (insofar as a general criticism is applicable) to keep the study of language as a remote science in its own right. They were obsessed by minor changes resulting, for example, in the preference or survival of one word instead of another. They accepted, often a trifle too readily, the assertion that speech was primarily a human prerogative. Many psychologists viewed this approach with favor. They were attracted by the intimate study of the meaningfulness of words. Words led to abstractions, abstractions to thoughts, and thereon to essentially human problems.

The majority of the important advances concerned with man and speech owe their origin to the indefatigable researches of the modern school of anthropology. The earlier anthropologists differed very considerably in their approach from those who have since raised anthropology to its present exalted status. They were interesting personalities, without doubt, but their researches were hardly worthy of the eponym of Science. Some may well have been disbelievers who gloated at the downfall of the *lingua adamaica.* Others were philologists who kept in fashion by espousing the cause of linguistic change. They were joined by a colorful collection of adventurers and explorers who gloried in their contact with the more primitive peoples of the globe. All were motivated by a common belief that they could develop a science of language, a *Sprachwissenschaft* as Max Muller termed it. They treated this science of linguistic symbols as separate and independent of all other sciences. *"La linguistique,"* wrote F. De Saussure, *"a pour unique et veritable objet la langue envisagee en elle-meme et pour elle-meme."*

No longer did they wonder whether perfection of language had ever been an universal attribute: it was now assumed that language arose from meager beginnings and became more elaborate with the course of time. "There is a movement in the whole vocabulary of language from the designation of what is coarser, gross, more material, to the designation of what is finer, more abstract and conceptual, more formal" (Dwight Whitney). The earlier anthropologists searched for a primitive language which in every aspect was rudimentary. Lowest on the scale of rudimentary tongues was that of the Arunta in Australia. Sommerfelt found that they had only three vowel sounds and no mixed vowel forms and that their language was also debased in a great many other respects.

However, there were claims far beyond those of Sommerfelt. Perhaps of all these claims expressed in their many different ways, that of Mary H. Kingsley is best known. She achieved a fame equalling if not surpassing that of her uncle, the writer Charles Kingsley. As an attractive spinster in her early thirties she chose to disregard the gruesome stories of the cruelty of the

African continent, the savagery, cannibalism, nudity and sexual brutality which scandalized Victorian society, and travelled widely amongst the jungle peoples. Her two books, *Travels in West Africa* and *West African Studies*, were an immediate popular success. Before her death, met with as she served as a nurse in the Boer War, she had caused many myths to be buried but had erected others in their stead. "Five or six hundred pages of close print," wrote her biographer (Olive Campbell, *A Victorian in the Jungle*, 1957), "run on through brilliant descriptions, strange adventures, comic anecdotes, ethnological research, comprehensive study of native religion, and the history of African trade; and these many ingredients are so intermixed that you never know from page to page whether you will be listening to a treatise or Fetish or to a Thurberesque misadventure."

The indirect effects of her writings were socially, politically, commercially, even religiously, tremendous. From the scientific point of view, it was a pity that her powers of observation and deduction were accepted so uncritically. Her most important legacy to science is based upon the fallacious interpretation of one casual and erroneous impression that "the inhabitants of Fernando Po, the Bubis, are quite unable to see the accompanying gestures of the conversation; . . . they frequently said: we will go to the fire so we can see what they say—when any question had to be decided after dark." A whole generation accepted this statement to mean that these people were so primitive as not to possess a language which could be expressed without gesture. The statement was accepted by a number of eminent men of science who chose without corroborative data to incorporate it verbatim into their own suppositions of a gestural origin of language, supposing that man at sometime in his early days had conversed in silence through gesture before the dawn of vocal speech. There is no means of telling from her description whether the inhabitants to which she refers represented a mixed group of peoples with several dialects or languages or whether they all were of the same tongue. Neither is it clear whether they approached the fire for their own intercommunication or in order that the observers, including, one may presume, Mary Kingsley, could better follow the tenor of their talk. Each presupposes a different explanation. Mary Kingsley undoubtedly alerted people to the possibility of a kinship between primitive speech and gesture but she can only be said to have commented upon the possibilities.

The hunt was on for the absolute rudiments of language and these were sought in many and varied ways. Etymologists, for example, tried to retrace the development of modern language. This might be called the backwards approach:

Philosophers who chase
A panting syllable through time and space,
Start it at home, and hunt it in the dark
To Gaul, to Greece and into Noah's Ark.

In most hands the results of their researches were plainly absurd, but Jespersen, by this unlikely approach, has obtained information of the greatest scientific value.

Others tried to visualize the circumstances in which language might have arisen, and thereby have produced a series of nativistic theories many of which have been quaintly dubbed with memorable epithets, largely at the hand of the German philologist, Max Muller. For the populace his lectures marked an important historical landmark. He was essentially a showman. He flayed the dour evolutionists and mocked all theories which did not accord with his personal whims. A tangential thought would lead to a clever paradox or give rise to an arresting etymological statement. He surpassed Mary Kingsley in mastery of the anecdotal knack, style and enthusiasm which can turn philology into a fascinating, light and relaxing pursuit.

The most telling phrase of Muller's is that with which he damned the onomatopoeic theory of Leibniz and Steinthal. They believed in language made up through imitation of natural sounds: the noises of nature and the mimicry of animal cries. They were able to show that some of the older languages, for instance, Egyptian, Manchu and Basque, were especially rich in onomatopoeic words and that such words were present in all languages at all levels of civilization. Words like "quack," "miaow," "croak," "roar," "splash" and "sneeze" may be quoted as examples. Muller dubbed this theory as the "bow-wow"

hypothesis, for to him, words like "cuckoo" were essentially sterile and their meanings inextensible. "The onomatopoeic theory goes very smoothly as long as it deals with cackling hens and quacking ducks, but around that poultry yard there is a high wall, and we soon find that it is behind that wall that language really begins."

Muller supposed a mysterious or psychological harmony between sound and sense in language, "Every impression from without received its vocal expression from within . . . Thus all words, expressive of immaterial conceptions, are derived by metaphores from words expressive of sensible ideas, a harmony of sound, thing and action. The link between sound and meaning may be obvious, mysterious or explicable psychologically." But this theory, called by Herder the "ding-dong" hypothesis, is scarcely more extensible.

Several theories have supposed that language was inherent in man and arose involuntarily: as interjections of pain or delight—the pooh-pooh theory; as part of the automatic activity of the laryngeal sphincter—the colly-wobble theory; or as involuntary sounds accompanying bodily effort—the yo-heave-ho theory if the effort is strenuous, and the yum-yum theory for that accompanying eating. And there have been others who have argued that communication by gesture preceded speech—the ta-ta hypothesis—that *homo locquitor* was preceded by *homo alalus.*

Gesture, bodily movement and involuntary noises were harnessed by Donovan into the *Festal Origin of Speech*—the tarara-boom-de-ay hypothesis. He was impressed by the manner in which rhythmic dances affect people, making them more extroverted and encouraging their participation in every conceivable way. If they cannot beat the tune they may call it out so that their voices take on a rhythmicity and a discipline necessary for speech. This was said to account for the phonetic structure and the symbolic basis of language. This theory has been resurrected by Jespersen who noted the way in which the older works of European literature were structurally more rigid,

relied more on prosody and alliteration, and were usually given a musical form. He envisaged speech and music emerging from an earlier form that included both. "Primitive language," he declared, "was musical and passionate."

Revesz has produced a new distinctive theory that language arose from herd instinct, a need for contact with his fellows: there was a transition from the cry addressed to the herd at large, to the call having a more individual appeal, and later to the word. But man's interjections, like the cries of an animal, are undisciplined, uncouth noises, that cannot be given a phonetic value; and besides, why should the contact of the herd produce speech in man but not in other animals?

One admires the ingenuity of these attractive hypotheses with their facetious names, but whether they are taken separately or collectively, it is hard to be convinced that they provide an adequate answer to the origins of speech. The discoveries of Natural Selection and Evolution recognized in the latter half of the nineteenth century provided the initial impetus for research of a scientific kind into speech and its origins. At the beginning of the twentieth century, ethnological study among primitive peoples and the discovery of the fossil remains and implements of early man provided a very real spur to research on an anthropological basis. It may be said, cynically yet factually, that the late result of the equalizing theories of evolution—that man was akin to the animals—was to cause the vicious doctrine of Aryan supremacy to be presumed to be scientific.

Chapter 3

ANIMAL COMMUNICATION

Man: "a hairy quadruped, furnished with a tail and pointed ears probably arboreal in his habits,"
from DARWIN's Descent of Man, 1871.

"the ape in trousers,"
C. S. LEWIS

THE SUBJECT OF animal communication has yet to be adequately explored. A hundred years after the publication of the *Origin of Species* we are only just beginning to develop experimentation into the subject. To draw fast conclusions based upon the present state of knowledge would be hazardous indeed. It is necessary to be aware of the semantic distinctions between speech, language and communication. One may repeat Revesz differentiation of cry, call and word, each representing a more directed and more thoughtful vocalization. As Meillet says, many animals emit various sounds to various ends. But whatever their precision and variety, these different sounds, for example, the miaowings of a cat, never express anything but a desire or an appeal. They never seem to communicate a fact.

Purposeful communication, vocal and non-vocal, exists among animals; and we can agree that the faculty for articulate speech does not offer any insuperable objection to the belief that man has developed from some lower form. Communication of a chemical kind exists among the lowest forms of life. Communication of a visual nature, through movements, and communication through expressive sounds are also widespread. The hive dances of honey-bees transmitting information to others about the direction, distance and nature of a food source is an example of visual communication; the mating and warning calls of birds, an example of vocal communication. Gillespie's account of the alternating trumpetings which form the courting ritual of penguins suggests that such communication cannot be dismissed lightly. The two birds stand a few feet apart and address each other with a delicious air of formality and correctness. Each penguin is most careful never to interrupt the other. His partner unhurriedly completes the final note and relaxes in anticipation of the reply. The ability to mime the vocalizations of other species is seen among many birds bred in captivity and not a few in the wild state. If the mimicking of expression or movement is considered, almost all higher mammals are expert in the art. The communication of animals is highly complex. It is, as Schwidetzky said, "simpler to translate thirty pages of Cicero than to define the meaning of a crocodile's grunt."

There still exists today the traditional divide between those who declare that animals are without speech and those equally confident that the reverse is true. Wilde, von Humboldt, Elliott Smith, Muller and Paget may all be quoted against the idea of animal speech. Wilde said that there is no mode of action, no form of emotion that we do not share with the lower animals. It is only by language that we rise above them—by language which is the parent, and not the child, of thought. Darwin, Lorenz and Schwidetzky are convinced that animal speech is a reality. "Do not despise the humble ape, It helped your native speech to shape!" It was Darwin's belief that the lower animals differ from man solely in his almost infinitely larger power of associating together the most diversified sounds and ideas, and this obviously depends on the high development of his mental powers.

A claim made in the past and occasionally repeated is that animal vocalizations are innate whereas those of humans have to be learned, only the capacity for speech being innate. But it has been shown by Daines Barrington, in Darwin's day, that the songs of some birds are normally learned from other members of the species. In this knowledge, Darwin attempted to analyze still further the points of difference. The use of meaningful vocalization is by no means confined to man, but lower animals differ from man in that they possess a lesser degree of ability to associate diverse sounds and ideas, and the use of articulate language is habitual only in man. Man also uses in common with the lower animals inarticulate cries to express his meaning; these cries are aided by gestures and movements of the muscles of the face—this is especially so with the more simple and vivid feelings which are but little connected with our higher intelligence. Our cries of pain, fear, surprise, anger, together with their appropriate actions, and the murmur of a mother to her beloved child, are more expressive than any words. That which distinguishes man from the lower animals is not the understanding of articulate sounds, for, as everyone knows, dogs understand many words and sentences. In this respect they are in the same stage of development as infants between the ages of ten and twelve months, who understand many words and short sentences, but cannot as yet utter a single word. It is not the mere articulation which is our distinguishing character, for parrots and other birds possess this power. Nor is it the mere capacity for connecting definite sounds with definite ideas; for it is certain that some parrots, which have been taught to speak, connect unerringly words with things, and persons with events.

Human cries can be readily distinguished from human speech. The frequency range of speech is limited, even monotonous, and little attention is paid to its pitch, noise or rapidity of utterance. In contrast, the abruptness, pitch and noise of a cry are all-important—the syllabic structure never merits attention. A cry need have no modulating association with any other cries; its frequency range is free and adds to its impact. It is scarcely surprising that many philologists prefer not to incorporate these vocalizations within the definition of speech or language. To such people Darwin's conclusion is unacceptable; thus Diamond, while recognizing the psychological continuity underlying the use of animal cries and some of the uses of language, takes issue with Darwin over any possibility of a continuity between animal sounds and the phonetic elements of speech.

Further phonological differences have been described by Stein and Kalaman. Kalaman, as a result of a careful anatomical comparison of the larynx of man and that of other animals, concluded that man-like vocalization is not possible among apes, so that even if an ape were to possess the mental capacity for speech he would still be unable to speak. The laryngeal sounds of animals, according to Stein, remain unmodified. Speech sounds depend on the use of the lips, tongue and palate and these seem to have been utilized in the first place by man. He might have added that for an inarticulate human cry modification of the laryngeal sound by movement of the lips, tongue or palate does not occur.

The vocal cords of primates are harder and sharper edged than those of man. It is possible with perseverence to teach a young chimpanzee to say a few words of human speech—mama, papa, cup or up—but he will do so in an abrupt, plosive fashion (see Cathy and Keith Hayes, *The Ape in Our Home*). But Stein's claim does not go unchallenged. Schwidetzky was able to show that the lips and tongue could play a part in animal communication. He listed the tongue click and lip clacks of macaques, the lip click of orangutans, the lateral clicks of young mandrills and the bilabial *p* and *r* sounds of gibbons. Furthermore he was able to demonstrate the presence of these same sounds among the phonetic symbols of many languages, Zulu, Anamite, Bushman, Old Chinese, and even Indo-Germanic. As a tour-de-force he claimed a similarity between the predominant blood groups of the races using these sounds and the primates whence they came. This theory, in fact, fits in with Leakey's more recent belief that man came not from one stem but from at least three.

It is never easy to evaluate such observations. They depend upon a series of imponderables that can only be checked upon by further observation. This is the great difficulty in the evaluation of progress in animal communication. Revesz is especially critical of research started without any precise "concept of speech." His definition could well take the form of a semantic spoonerism: the concept of speech and the speech of concept. Indeed, the most commonly quoted difference between human speech and its zoological equivalent centers around man's use of verbal symbols in speech, a fact correctly ascribed to his superior mentation. Speech, it is said, is man's invention, and although he may not be alone in his capacity to invent—the beaver may dam a stream, the sparrow build a nest—his capacity for invention is on a far, far higher plane than that of any animal. Most definitions of speech depend on this conceptual approach; yet a definition of this kind provides a narrower basis for speech than even Darwin's distinction between articulate and inarticulate utterances. If the definition of speech is confined to ability to communicate to another or even to oneself by a chain of logical thought expressed as articulated sounds it becomes impossible to contend on the available evidence that animals have speech. They neither form difficult words nor possess a grammar with main and subordinate clauses, nouns, verbs, adjectives, and prepositions. If the argument is continued, it is also evident by this standard, as Schwidetzky has remarked, that speech cannot even be accorded to small children.

For a more thorough appraisal of animal communication it is necessary to descend from the general to the particular. Professor R. M. Yerkes has listed a wide range of noises made by chimpanzees and other apes but has always held that the term speech could not be applied fittingly to these utterances: "although evidence of use of the voice and of definite word-like sounds to symbolize feelings, and possibly ideas, becomes increasingly abundant from lemur to ape, no one of the infra-human primates exhibits a systematization of vocal symbols which may approximately be described as speech." In *The Great Apes*, he repeats the same thought in a telling phrase, commenting that the vocalizations of these primates "cannot be used between meals to talk over the merits of the feast." Apes are, by and large, silent creatures. They find that they can best convey their desires through gestures which commonly involve the whole body. They express their emotions and indicate their wishes and control over one another's behavior by gesture and example. Sir Richard Paget, in *Human Speech* (1930), fastens on to a suggestion of Professor Yerkes from his book, *Almost Human*, that apes may perhaps be taught to gesture with their fingers more easily than they may be taught speech and suggests that if a deaf-mute were to rear a baby chimpanzee, conversing with it through gesture, and if the deaf-mute teacher were sympathetic and the young chimpanzee were of average intelligence, then the initiation of the chimpanzee into sign language would very likely succeed. Paget was renowned for his enthusiasm for gesture communication but his opinion is perhaps not altogether eccentric as most observers do not presume fundamental differences between human and primate gestural capacity.

Lilly has abandoned the attempt to study speech in monkeys and has turned instead to exploration of the possibility of speech in bottle-nosed dolphins. His hypothesis is that the failure of the chimpanzee to be taught speech is due to the small size of his brain which is a quarter that of a human adult and under half that of a human child when it first learns to speak. For this reason he transferred his attentions to a mammal whose brain weight and brain weight per unit of body length more closely approximates that of the human adult. Dolphins also have similarly prolonged periods of maternal dependence and instruction.

The intercommunication of dolphins is based on an echo sounding mechanism at a much higher pitch than the range of the human voice, but some sounds do overlap. Whereas the human voice ranges between 100 c/s to a little over 5,000 c/s, dolphins emit noises at between 3,000 to 20,000 c/s within the range of human audibility with other bands up to a limit of 120,000 c/s. Lilly makes the claim that these noises are meaningful and that if a dolphin is trained by prolonged and early human contact he can adapt his noises to mimic human vocalization. Lilly kept dolphins in an experimental tank inside his laboratory and recorded the dolphin noises shortly after he had been dictating to his secretary. He played the tape at half speed and then at third speed. Eureka, he heard none other than a high speed rendering of his conversation. Much more work has been done on dolphin speech by Lilly and his colleagues and still more remains to be done. But to where will it all lead?

If Lilly's findings are correct, another point of interest emerges. The dolphin's fins are adapted solely for swimming, they have no other purpose. It has been frequently claimed that the manipulative skills of the human hand have provided the formulative need for human speech, but there is no question of the dolphin having an appendage equivalent to the human hand. The vocal apparatus of the dolphin is adapted for sonar transmission. Sound and ultrasonic waves are utilized on the echo principle to determine the depth of the seabed and the nearness of objects. A similar form of space determination is used by bats. There is nothing new in point of fact in a sense organ or a muscular mechanism becoming specialized to subserve a very different purpose to that for which it was originally intended.

Animal communication is a vast unknown replete with many surprises. Research into the noises of animals is respectable and of immense scientific interest. Let us await the future with cautious enthusiasm and interest.

Chapter 4

WALLACE AND THE GESTURAL THEORY

"Must a name mean something?" Alice asked, doubtfully.
"Of course it must," Humpty Dumpty said with a short laugh, "My name means the shape I am, and a good handsome shape it is, too. With a name like yours, you might be any shape, almost."

LEWIS CARROLL, *Alice through the Looking Glass*

THE GESTURAL THEORY, however expressed, regards language as primarily visual, and seeks its origin in the hand, the mouth, and in the joints of the body. The pantomime of the body furnishes the vital impulse reflected in the word which is basically the embodiment of gesture and bears the imprint of its spatial and motor origin. Words have shapes, textures and hues. The gesture theory is not a unitary concept of the origin of language, there are many varieties of the theory, but it is one of the two main conjectural themes concerned with the birth of language. Language has been thought of as arising either from an increased auditory awareness and discrimination of sounds in the environment or from an association of vocal and bodily movement, later elaborated, pruned and refined.

Among the ancients the relationship of gesture to speech was frequently discussed. One may quote Plato or perhaps Cicero's advice to actors in *De Oratore*, "The action of the hand should not be too affected but should follow the words rather than express them by mimicry." The gestural hypothesis of language lingered in obscurity until it was referred to by Max Muller in the course of his lectures on the Science of Language, in London in 1864. Two years earlier a certain Dr. Rae had published three articles in Honolulu (*The Polynesian,* September 27, October 4, and October 11, 1862) on the significance of mouth-gestures from an anthropological standpoint. He had been rightly acclaimed as the originator of the gestural hypothesis and his articles are preserved as an appendix to Sir Richard Paget's *Human Speech* (Kegan Paul, 1930, London). But Alfred Russel Wallace, Darwin's coauthor of the *Theory of Natural Selection,* has been credited by Paget (*Science News,* 1951) as "the first to propound a serious theory" (of gesture) to account for the earliest origin of language. This relationship of the gestural hypothesis with the evolutionists is not commonly recognized and it is perhaps of value to consider the significance of Wallace's contribution to the subject.

Wallace's interest in mouth-gesture and speech acquisition was first shown in his anthropological essays (1864, 1869 and 1870), according to H. F. Osborn (1913). But his first clear statement of this theory is found in a review in 1881 of E. B. Tylor's *Researches into the Early History of Mankind.* The expanded theory was then published in the *Fortnightly Review* in 1895, under the title "Expressiveness of Speech: On Mouth Gesture, A Factor in the Origin of Language." But one must turn to a still later publication (*Studies Scientific and Social*) for an explanation of the development of his thoughts:

> My attention was first directed to this subject by noticing that, when Malays were talking together, they often indicated direction by pouting out their lips. They would do this either silently, referring to something already spoken or understood, but more frequently when saying *disane* (there) or *itu* (that), thus avoiding any further explanation of what was meant.
>
> At the same time, I did not see the important bearing of this gesture; but many years afterwards, when paying some attention to the imitative origin of language, it occurred to me that while pronouncing the words in question, impressively, the mouth would be opened and the lips relatively protruded, while the same thing would occur with our corresponding English words "there" and "that;" and when I saw further that the French "la" and "cela," and the German "da" and "das," had similar open-mouthed pronunciation, it seemed probable that an important principle was involved."

Darwin never expressed himself as firmly as Wallace on gesture-speech relationships, but his writings, especially the *Expression of the Emotions in Man and Animals* (1872), are often cited in favor of a gestural hypothesis. He classified human gestures. There were those such as shrugging the shoulders as a sign of impotence and raising the arms with wide open hands and extended fingers as a sign of wonderment which were innate and equivalent to the tail-wagging, baring of the teeth and arching of the back seen in animals. They are used less often and are considered artificial or conventional but nonetheless they are basic to all human races. Other forms of gesture may be familial traits for they may be common to certain members of a family. And yet other gestures, so natural that we might easily imagine that they are innate, seem to be learned like the words of a language. This may be the case with the joining of uplifted hands in prayer. "Every true or inherited movement of expression seems to have had some natural and independent origin. But when once acquired, such movements may be voluntarily and consciously employed as a means of communication. Even infants, if carefully attended to, find out at a very early age that their screaming brings relief, and they soon voluntarily practice it."

Just as Hughlings Jackson drew a sharp distinction between what he called propositional speech and ejaculatory or emotional utterances, so is it also possible to break down gesture and seek out its most rudimentary forms. Signs appear on the highest rung of the evolutionary ladder for they represent discrete, limited, conventional movements of, say, the hand; their symbolism is not directly descriptive of the idea intended to be expressed. Thus finger spelling as used by the deaf or deafblind is a language of letters, which when purely applied, devoid of other movements, transmits meaning as accurately as speech or the written word. Gesture, in its limited sense, is used for a spontaneously invented and descriptive movement, usually of the hand or head, to express an idea. Gesticulation is restricted to those gestural movements which accompany rather than replace speech. At a lower level we can distinguish between grimaces, usually facial and involving striated muscle—smiling, sneering, frowning and snarling; and facial mimetic phenomenon —pallor and flushing—depending on unstriped muscle and representing vestiges of widespread autonomic responses. Darwin regarded blushing as an autonomic response peculiar to man. The various hypotheses invoking gesture each concentrate on one aspect of gestural evolution and upon this graft an elementary speech mechanism. Lowest of the low is the colly-wobble theory, or ontogenetic hypothesis, basing speech upon the automatic activity of the laryngeal sphincter—a laryngeal flatulence.

Man had necessarily to undertake tasks involving strenuous bodily effort. Not surprisingly this fact provides the basis of several of the hypotheses. The progression of reptiles and fishes entails a writhing, athetoid movement of the whole body. Mammalia, and particularly man, have cortico-spinal tracts of nerve fibers enabling more discrete movements to be performed; yet in performing any especially strenuous task almost all the bodily musculature is thrown into action, and sound—the rudiments of speech—is emitted involuntarily in the performance of the task. This principle—that speech arose involuntarily during action—was first enunciated by Norrie and has been tagged the yo-heave-ho, or ta-ta hypothesis. Diamond has quite recently revived the hypothesis, postulating that man would naturally turn to speech when his hands and body are embroiled in a task requiring every ounce of strength. He would need to direct his friends to come to his aid. The likely first words would be those with a definite purpose, imperatives such as "cut," "break," "crush" or "strike." Paget's click-clack theory is somewhat similar, linking movement of the muscles of articulation with those of the arms, and the Icelandic etymologist, Johannesson, has claimed that the origins of certain expressive morphemes, can be traced in remote ancestral gesture.

Johannesson's theory is in fact an acknowledged restatement and elaboration of the observations of mouth-gesture or lip-pointing made by Rae and Wallace. Rae was entranced by man's mimetic ability and believed language originated through the application of this art. He argued that sound by its very nature is very confined in its capacity to suggest an idea of an external object because it has no resemblance to it. It would seem almost limited to the representation of the cries of animals and therefore also of the animals uttering them. But when we utter an articulate sound, we call into play the breath, the lips, the tongue, the cheeks, and these are things of which the nature and action may be recognized by the senses; they have resemblances to the objects making up what we call the visible world. There may therefore be analogies with these objects shaped in the course of speech and these may be sufficiently close to indicate, or suggest, or serve to recall them to the mind.

Likewise, Wallace was of the opinion that the pantomimic use of the various parts of the mouth constitutes "a fundamental principle which has always been at work both in the origin and in the successive modifications of human speech." Over and above Darwin's famous comment on the sympathy of hand and mouth in conveying meaning, Wallace maintained that many words had originated out of the attempt to make gestures with the mouth either with or without the aid of the hands. He considered that for primitive man, mouth gesture words would have been earliest: "He had, as it were, to struggle hard to make himself understood, and would, therefore, make use of every possible indication of meaning offered by the positions and motions of mouth, lips and breath, in pronouncing each word; and he would lay stress upon and exaggerate these indications, not slur them over as we do."

At one stage in his discourse Wallace stipulated that mouth gestures would have been used in preference to hand gestures in times of emergency and from crouching positions when the hands were not free; from this it would be only a step to turn them into noises for communication in the dark. This is to say that Wallace was among the many who subscribe to the theory of *homo alalus,* a mute ancestor of *homo sapiens,* and presumably, if the argument is logically pursued, an ancestor devoid of even the vocalization of the other primates. Their careless sounds, according to this theory, would hinder the development of meaningful speech.

If the concept of a voiceless predecessor, *homo alalus,* is unappealing, Wallace's explanation of the primary need for speech, has considerable superficial merit and is germane to the wider aspects of the discussion; to what Leopald Stein termed the *Infancy of Speech and the Speech of Infancy.*

"We are apt to forget," Wallace wrote, "that, though speech

is now acquired by children solely by imitation, and must be to them almost wholly conventional, this was not its original character. Speech was formed and evolved not by children, but by men and women who felt the need of a communication other than by gesture only. Gesture language and word language doubtless arose together, and for a long time were used in conjunction and supplemented each other." (Note the inherent contradiction between this and his earlier statement.)

A. S. Diamond (1959) is one of the few who have discussed the original purpose of speech in a context similar to that of Wallace: "For what purpose was speech required? Not for the purposes of men as a member of his famly. Not for the purposes of the relations between a man and his wife: woman is still wooed and wedded, and the spouses still cohabit, with hardly a word spoken. The same applies to the relations between parents and children as such. Physical sustenance and comfort, warning cries of alarm and visual example—these, not words, are the things most needed for the rearing of the family. For what, then, is speech necessary in so simple a community? There is only one thng left—to obtan an action by others which we cannot do for ourselves: to request action by our fellows."

In his appreciation of lip-pointing among the Malay people, Wallace can be said to have found a primitive gesture used by a people at a level of civilization far above the primitive Sakai, Semang or Dyaks of the archipelago. The Malay language contains a curious mixture of rudimentary terms such as plurals or totally different meanings achieved by duplication of words, e.g., "mata" meaning an eye and "mata-mata" meaning a policeman, many borrowings from Arabic and a grammatical structure of great simplicity which has come about in the past three or four centuries. This fact and the recognition of lip-pointing among other peoples—in Brazil and in the Polynesian Islands—suggests that it was once a universal form of communication. It could represent the transference of a fairly simple and elementary hand gesture to the face. Wallace supposed that lip-pointing may have been molded into a speech form in words to be found in a wide variety of languages, expressing ideas such as coming and going, inward and outward, self and others, up and down. Then again, motions of almost every kind are usually clearly indicated by the use of expressive terminal letters which have a natural basis in the corresponding motions of the organs of speech; and physical qualities of various kinds are similarly indicated. He even suggested tentatively that some of the mental and moral qualities of man, as well as many of his actions and sensations, are more or less clearly expressed by means of other forms of speech-gesture.

It may be wrong to regard mouth gesture as a more highly developed form of gesture than hand gesture. The facility for movement of individual fingers is not greatly developed in the higher primates and Leakey, in his study of Zinjanthropus fossils in Olduvan Gorge in Tanzania, concluded that the use of primitive tools began before the hand itself had evolved so as to oppose thumb and little finger. In early man the use of hand gesture must have been relatively crude but the muscles of facial expression, both in man and in the apes, are numerous and refined. Certainly there has been a change in the grossness of facial movement needed to convey an expression between primate and man and between savage and civilized man; thus in conversation the teeth and tongue remain unexposed for the most part but every now and again—probably more so in primates and presumably so in early man—in the course of an articulated utterance the teeth and tongue are exposed in a clear and significant manner.

Teachers of the deaf, training their pupils to understand by lipreading, speak more slowly than an average person, prolong their syllables and exaggerate the movements of their lips and tongue. They may reveal the teeth and show the tongue when making the "th" sound. This may have been somewhat akin to the manner of speaking employed by our ancestors; that we unconsciously lipread to a certain degree in our daily conversation has been shown countless times experimentally. The spoken word may be understood at a much lower volume if the face of the speaker is visible than when his face is hidden. A coarse form of speech, exaggerating the lip movements, increases the kinesthetic feedback from the articulatory muscles to the "speech centers," so that whether or not gesture preceded speech it is certainly true that there was more "feel" in primitive speech.

The gestural hypothesis of speech has been taken many stages further. To Paget human speech was "essentially a branch of human gesture which the ear has learnt to identify—without the aid of sight—by means of its secondary effects in modifying the resonances produced by the passage of air by and through the gesticulating members of the vocal cavity." Mankind, he said, had a natural faculty for symbolizing "ungesturable" ideas by the method of analogy. Thus one cannot invent a natural gesture for *true* or *false*, or for *remember* or *forget*, or for *perhaps*. But Paget went outside speech to observe the natural sign language, "so similar to each other as almost to be one and the same," used by American Indians and deaf-mutes. A highly developed form of gesture communication in "natural sign language" is used by American Indians when communicating with members of other tribes as each tribe has its own dialect or even its own language. Thus, although speech was the natural means of communication within a tribe, if in the course of its wanderings it chanced upon another tribe, they would converse through gesture. To them "true" was "straight talk" or that very masonic expression "on the square;" "lie" was "two tongues" or "that which cuts across the mouth," i.e., across the spoken word; "perhaps" was "two hearts"—the heart being considered by the American Indians as the seat of the mind—or it was "this way and that" or "good and bad alternating." In other words, both in speech where the vocabulary was limited and in sign language, abstract or other ungesturable ideas were instinctively symbolized by reference to gesturable ideas which illustrated them or were felt to be related to them.

In modern life, it may be said that we have inherited so vast a vocabulary of ready-made words that we are not often called upon to invent verbal symbols for ourselves in this way; but when the need does arise, and it is often in relation to the highest "manifestation" of scientific achievement, we fall back on analogies based on the same principle. If, for example, we discuss the brain in this context, our analogies are almost historical in their conception. The vestibular connections, dis-

covered by Magnus at the end of the last century, are likened
to a Heath Robinson contraption of pulleys and wires; the
reticular formation to the flux between an electric battery and a
condensor, the hypothalamus to a melting pot of multifarious
biochemical systems and the parietal cortex to a vast computer.

In adult conversation, audible speech and gesture readily
combine. The freedom with which the two are mixed varies
with the personality of the speaker, his mood—whether manic
or depressed—and characteristics inherent in his race. Where
gestures are at their most flamboyant, so, commonly, is the
speech also flamboyant; the pitch varies considerably—the voice
is a shout one minute and a whisper the next—the rate of speaking increases as the words ascend the musical scale, and, perhaps
most significantly, the pictorial imagery of the vocabulary, more
flamboyant than all else, is accompaned by gestures of apt and
delicate mime. Conversely, among the impassive and taciturn,
neither imagery nor speech is permitted to vary, and gesture
must wither as though it never did exist. These people are
considered "dry,' for, though language is capable of being
divorced from the crude display of the emotions, some vestige
of the emotions in the form of mimetic play helps to gain the
sympathy of the listener. Intelligent persons may be able to
emphasize by a fleeting movement that they are seeking
vocabulary-wise for *le mot juste* and thus heighten the impact
of their utterance informing their audience that the phrase they
are about to enunciate is "liquid gold." It increases their own
care for their use of language for having made, almost acci-
dentally, some extravagant flourish they will strive to match it
with a pithy or choice expression. But for a lazy person, gestures
may be used from sheer slovenliness to substitute for something
which ought to have been more exactly expressed in speech.

In certain circumstances children may find that the world
of gesture provides an easier access to the fulfillment of their
wants than can be attained through the more arduous medium
of speech. Watts, for whom language is something to be carefully
nurtured in the young and to be studied in its poetic perfection
by the old, deplores the supplanting of even the crudest circum-
locutions by gestures. "It is hardly necessary to say that some

social and educational environments are more favorable to speech development than are others. Those teachers who work in slum districts know only too well that a few nouns eked out by a few gestures can be made to describe or explain a great deal, and that to get children to make the effort to speak with greater fluency and precision is by no means a simple task. The appropriate verb, in particular, appears to be less easily acquired in a poor linguistic environment than most nouns. If we listen to the conversation of a group of uneducated persons we may notice that they are least precise where their verbs are concerned. In a world where we are often pressed for time and looked to constantly for sympathy we are apt to take a meaning for granted when not always adequately expressed. Therefore, the parent or teacher who is really interested in the linguistic progress of children would do well, occasionally, to misunderstand deliberately though good humoredly when he is sure that a little effort would make the young speaker's meaning very much clearer both to himself and to others."

Lovell and many others interested in the education of deaf children, firmly adhere to the belief that if a child develops a system of gesture language, and his parents understand him, he may not take the trouble to talk. There has always been a strong eugenic argument against the use of natural signs among deaf children, for if a deaf child learns to communicate by gestures alone, he will be limited to the company of other deaf children who understand sign language and hence become an outcast from society. Children pick up speech most readily in their early years and the danger that the child may miss the opportunity to learn to speak adequately exists, despite the fact that it is a gross over-simplification to regard sign language and speech in deaf children as mutually incompatible. The speed of natural sign language through gesture is far faster than oral speech among deaf chldren and outstrips and breaks up the lip movements which frequently accompany it. If a deaf child is addressed in natural sign language the desire to reply orally is decreased, the medium of words is lost and the understanding of the written word is retarded by reason of the innate imprecision of gestural symbolism. There is reason to believe that the use of finger spelling and even of the combined system (finger spelling and conventional gestures) is much less detrimental to speech development and may even assist the acquisition of literary knowledge and a broadly based vocabulary.

The relationship of gesture to the origin of speech has been analyzed in detail by Macdonald Critchley. He regards gesture as the "elder brother" of speech rather than as the actual ancestor. "More probably," he declares, in a paragraph dismissing the notion of a prehistoric *homo alalus*, "mimetic movements as well as verbalization both grew up in concert, and blossomed side by side in symbolic elaboration." It may be that the increasing strides made in the scientific study of animal communication will reveal a form of zoological articulation clearly akin to speech among animals unable to gesticulate in normal circumstances. Claims for such animal vocalization have been made by Schmidt in poultry, Von Madey and von Unruh in horses, Romer in cats and Lilly in dolphins. If these prove to be true, gesture will have to be considered as the younger brother of speech, a later development of the desire to communicate.

The development of speech may have had a long and stormy passage. We all know of families today where the members, though living together, have not spoken to each other for years, or, less dramatically, where the members of the family never "open up" to one another. If this same situation is transcribed to primitive food-gathering man, living in small and closely-related units, it is possible to visualize countless occasions when speech might temporarily dry up, whereas gesture, with its greater durability, would survive. In such circumstances, pointing to one's belly may indicate hunger and other equally primitive gestures suffice. Words might fail to be transmitted from father to son; and speech though showing a steady progression through previous generations would be lost save for a shout of exasperation at a missed meaning or an unobserved gesture. Words must have arisen and been forgotten and new words created in their place on the same tenuous foundation. In such contingencies, though speech may become suppressed in favor of gesture, mimetic activity refurnishes the desire to communicate and speech returns out of the desire for a better and more precise mode of communication.

Since Wallace's time, considerable research has been devoted to an attempt to verify his two main propositions—that the pantomimic principle may be still active in man's unconscious development of his spoken language, and that modern languages may be just as gestural as the older ones.

Johannesson studied the lip and tongue movements which he considered to be unconscious imitations of hand gestures. The basis of his study was the roots or morphemes of guttural sounds present in six apparently unrelated languages. He found consonants with like meanings in languages as diverse as Icelandic and Hebrew. Eighty-five per cent of 320 Indo-European roots were presumed to be explicable as pantomimic mouth gestures. Of seventy-eight Hebrew words chosen at random, 80 per cent were found to be gestural and similarly the gestural theory was evident in the structure of the Sumerian language.

Wallace's second proposition, as elucidated by Johannesson, has taken on a different form. The movements of the tongue, except in the fleeting movements when it is thrust forward between the teeth, do not comply with the earlier hypothesis which regarded language as purely visual. Linguistic roots must be unconsciously imitated and are at most only partly seen. The link between gesture and speech may be a kinesthetic one. In a gesture the joint position receptors "feed back" through the sensory pathways information confirming the adopted position and similarly the muscles concerned in articulation relay to the sensorium a series of impulses related to the motion and changes of posture through which they pass. This forms an important adjuvant to speech formation and is in fact made great use of in teaching deaf children to talk. If we accept Johannesson's theorem that 80 to 85 per cent of linguistic roots are in fact unconscious imitations of both purposive and symbolic hand actions, we can put forward two alternative hypotheses to explain how this might have come about. There may have been a gestural retreat whereby gross lip movements and frequent tongue protrusions have become less evident through the centuries. Or, it may be that a sound which entails a kinesthetic pattern similar to the kinesthetic pattern of a related hand action will be better retained in the memory than one with no such association. The association could be deliberate or it might have occurred through chance by Natural Selection, being plastic except in so far as genetic influences determine the shape of the larynx and the relative facility with which various sounds are produced.

Important, though indirect, support for this proposition may be assumed from the following quotation from Daniel Jones'

An Outline of English Phonetics:

Practical experience in teaching pronunciation shows that consonants are as a rule best acquired by directing attention to tactile and muscular sensations, whereas in learning vowels it is necessary to direct attention more particularly to the acoustic qualities of the sounds. This does not mean that the learner is expected to acquire vowels by "simple imitation." On the contrary, he will find a knowledge of the organic formation of vowels of considerable use to him. But this knowledge is not in itself sufficient. The finer adjustments of the tongue have to be done by means of sensory control from the ear.

Chapter 5

SPEECH TODAY

". . . and he meant, he said he meant
Perhaps he meant, or partly meant,"
  TENNYSON, *Enoch Arden*

THE QUESTION, "What is speech today?" does not lend itself
to an easy answer. The speech of those preeminent in civilized
society, the recognized leaders, the executants and the origin-
ators, might be taken to exemplify man's highest achievement in
the realm of language for they have advanced the three essentials
which distinguish man's speech from the communication of
animalia. They are more capable of detachment, able to use
verbal symbols unfashioned by emotion. They are capable of
extending the meaning of words from the concrete to the abstract
and from the present to the past or even into the future. And
they are capable of that economy in the choice of words which
comes from the appreciation of essentials. But in greater
measure it is the *vox populi* which causes language to change
regardless of the choice of words or grammatical quibbles
passed down by the pedants of each age. Quite probably the
highest levels of linguistic use, and the so-called degenerate
conversation of the street and the language needs of primitive
communities extant today can all contribute something in our
quest for a greater understanding of the basis of speech. It is
only in the heart of society, as Itard had said, that man can attain
the preeminent position which is his natural destiny.

We are sometimes informed that, to appreciate the true
pristine beauty of a piece of music, we should listen to it in
solitude, or better still, in darkness. This will indeed allow
us to appreciate its perfection in a cool, Grecian mien. But for
the enchantment of that music to penetrate our mortal frames we

39

require added emotional and visual overtones. We need to know all about the conductor, the soloist, or perhaps the history of the orchestra. We need to hear the performance "live;" to see "how he does it;" and the music becomes more meaningful still if played in particularly auspicious circumstances.

A close parallel may be drawn with regard to language. If someone produces a new theorem in which we are keenly interested, we would wish to study it carefully by reading it. This may require considerable concentration on our part; our critical and analytical faculties may then be brought to bear in order to understand it; we may follow the argument step by step, appraise the style and, if need be, memorize the essentials or even the whole. How often have we said after a complex lecture, "That was a mouthful, I must wait till I can read it in print?" It is easier to expound on something which is highly intricate in all its detail, in the written rather than by the spoken word; and yet, despite all this, we may flock to hear someone whose writings we have frequently read, not necessarily expecting him to say anything different from what we have read, but just to hear him say it. We may thus assess "the man," feel confident in his research or wish to take everything he says in future "with a pinch of salt." By seeing him propound his views we may better remember his theorem and what he is driving at despite the fact that he will have to condense his views and may only be able to repeat a quarter of what he has written.

Some simplification is usually necessary in adapting the written word for radio and further compression of the substance is required for television. But the television appearance is nonetheless often regarded as the essential test of the authority of a man in his chosen field as though we were observing thereby the effects of a truth drug.

What then accounts for the apparent superiority of the spoken word over the written word? Sir Max Beerbohm in 1923 put it thus: "Writing, as a means of expression, has to compete with talking. The talker need not rely wholly on what he says, he has the help of his mobile face and hands, and of his voice, with its various inflections and its variable pace, whereby he may insinuate fine shades of meaning, quality and strengthen at will, and clothing naked words with color, make dead words live. But the written? He can express a certain amount through his handwriting, if he writes in a properly plastic way. But his writing is not printed in facsimile. It is printed in cold, mechanical, monotonous type. For his every effort he must rely wholly on the words he chooses, and on the order in which he ranges them, and on his choice among the few hard and fast symbols of punctuation. He must so use these slender means that they shall express all that he can express through his voice and face and hands, or all that he would express if he were a good talker."

The spoken word may be made to possess frank esthetic appeal. This appeal may be due to what Hughlings Jackson termed its propositionizing—the quality of its content. Alternatively the language itself may be beautiful in syntax, in phraseology, in color or because the words themselves have been chosen with precision, succinctness, aptness, fullness of meaning, accuracy of translation or scientific correctness. There are numerous physical factors which may lead to the attraction of the spoken word. The words may be enunciated with exceptional clarity, nicety of timing and effective modulation of the voice. These are attributes recognized in singing or in the recitation of poetry. Sometimes, in the modern world, it is the ability to shape a talk to fit a time schedule which gains cudos for the speaker even to the detriment of the wit and humour added to temper the utterance in order to achieve its maximum effect upon a demanding audience.

At the highest level of formal speech, the speaker may orate, harangue, persuade, clarify, dramatize or declaim: appealing alike to the intellect and the emotions. The words used may be surprisingly simple. The logical mind may, through speech, play upon the feelings of the audience. One may, alas, become lost in a web of words; but success depends upon a speaker's ability to harness plain words where others would wallow in a morass of multifarious neologisms.

The existence of primitive races presented to the Victorians a riddle which they notably failed to solve. They were aware of the fossil forms of animals and were able to present a sequence

of evolution for these animals backed by the full force of logic;
but for them Java man provided the sole evidence of the existence of man in a more anthropoid form. The Victorians therefore cast about among the primitive tribes for evidence of man's
earlier morphoses. Were these people throwbacks of earlier
civilizations? The Victorian evolutionist also wished to argue
that man had grown into his present form shaped by the
selective influence of the struggle for survival. It was assumed
that all lesser peoples had been exterminated in inter-tribal wars
or forced to forgo their natural habitat. It was not easy for the
successful Western Gentleman, conscious that he was at the
zenith of his powers, to accept that some savages, inhabitants
of the tropics, could, when granted the opportunity, achieve
similar academic standards.

As the result of the serious anthropomorphic study which
has taken place in this century, it is apparent that only a few
backward people, capable of utilizing only the simplest tools,
can really be considered to reflect in their lives the modes of
existence of Early Man. The Semang and Sakai of the Malayan
jungles and the Bushman of the Australian outback represent,
in their seminomadic way of life a means of subsistence dependent almost entirely on food-gathering. They contribute little
or nothing to the tillage of the land, and, instead, they roam in
small family groups over wide tracts of country, gathering
honey, roots, eggs, small rodents and fish. Their dwellings are
in keeping with the lack of permanence of their existence.
Often these consist of rain shelters where the aborigine may
recline for a few hours before breaking new ground. A barely
superior level of existence, but one enabling a greater concentration of people who can defend themselves from attack, is attained
by supplementing the food-gathering with more organized
hunting—the use of traps, stalking the prey and cornering larger
animals—and the achievement of a rudimentary agriculture as a
subordinated means of livelihood. These groups rarely venture
outside their territories. The individual lives his life within
narrow bounds and it is this limited range of contact and stimulus
which is of fundamental importance in understanding the
stability and slowness of change among the simpler societies

of man.

A French anthropologist once explained to me how he used to make contact with the primitive swamp dwellers in Vietnam. In the dry season he would get as far into the interior as he and his party could go, driving their cars along dried up river beds. Thereafter they would advance on foot, keeping in touch with each other by whistles, maintaining a steady direction with a compass, and hacking their way through the mangrove swamps. The whistles would serve to warn tribesmen of their arrival and would suggest that they came openly and peacefully. The Negritos would approach them cautiously under cover of the undergrowth. Once they were assured of the peaceful intent of the intruders they would emerge and lead them to their camp. The party would hand over a few simple gifts. Usually the Negritos would leave these gifts untouched and stand fully twenty feet from the visitors and stare at them. In their turn they would stare back. Eventually, after upwards of half an hour had elapsed, they would thaw and draw closer with the aid of gestures. Food would be exchanged for gifts and finally all sitting, an exchange of noises would occur.

Not all the tribes were Negrito, but the way of life was common to all. They were seminomadic, hunting and burning down acres of jungle to make clearings, where they could grow rice and other crops such as tapioca. After a few rotations of crops, the land would become exhausted and eroded and they would move to another spot to begin the same cycle anew. Each tribe remains ignorant of the whereabouts of its neighbours. It could so happen that within five kilometres of each other—this must be reckoned as nearly a day's journey in certain parts of the jungle—there might dwell two or more tribes, unaware of each other's presence, or, for that matter, of each other's language.

The discoverers of North America beheld a similar situation. Each tribe had its own language but for intercourse between tribes signs were universal and had been elaborated into a complex code. If Swedenburg's theory of a *homo alalus* were correct, this would be just the situation where one might reasonably expect to find tribal languages of extreme simplicity and tribes in which sign-talk had entirely supplanted speech. But this is not so. Among the primitive hunters, among tillers of the soil and even among the most primitive food-gatherers known to civilization, each community is seen to possess a highly developed language with a mature and complex morphology and syntax (Jespersen). They also possess a stock of cultural ideas and a technology that, simple as they are, could not conceivably have evolved or been transmitted without the aid of the possession of speech over thousands of years. The range of vocabulary may be small but the greeting to a visitor may be long and elaborate.

Bernstein divides language into two kinds: public language, used by less-educated sections of the population and involving a limited range of grammatical forms; and formal language which exploits to the fullest extent the possibilities of language for the interpretation of experience and the communication of emotions. Not everyone can claim to keep up a literary style in the exigencies of everyday life, to do so would be to appear remote and haughty. In conversation, and it is one of the most difficult attainments for a would-be author to write good conversation, the distinction between sentences and single words, as Bertrand Russell observed, does not exist. This lack of syntactical construction does not imply an absence of propositionizing—wit and repartee, the arresting, the unexpected and the impudent thrive upon this absence of syntax. Free conversation may center upon disputes discussed in healthy adult terms, no offense given, taken or implied. Both wit and adult disputation represent a high level of intellectual attainment. Unfortunately, street conversation contains much to be condemned. Speech may degenerate into *tittle-tattle* and the conversation then abounds with repeatedly introduced meaningless token phrases, familiarity clauses, intimacy clauses, verbal garbage or sympathetic circulatory sequences—"One does, doesn't one?" "Yes, you know;" "Well, I never;" "You see; "Well its like this, you see."

A simple story, say of someone being given the wrong change at a store would be full of irrelevances:

"Well, the other day . . . When was it? Let me see. It must have been . . . Well never mind. As I was saying, you see,

at least he tried it on, you see. But I did not let him get away
with it. I says to him, I says, that's the wrong change, I says.
I forget how much it was now, but you see, don't you. It's kind
of worrying when it happens, isn't it?" Damon Runyon stories
abound with similar utterances in the New York vernacular.

In England, Hogarth has drawn attention to social, regional
and even class distinctions in the content of speech. The phrase
"they say" or "they do" immediately suggests a strong social
bias. Really rubbishy street conversation is a murmur of polite
but empty cliche. The attempt has been made on countless
occasions to extrapolate information of value to etymologists
from this low level of speech. The breakdown of syntax may be
suggestive and the continued need to adjust one's terms of
familiarity with the listener by gesture or manneristic phrase may
be reminiscent of warring tribesmen seeking to parley. But it
must be remembered that the needs fulfilld by such small talk
in the easy world of the multiple store, "dumb shopping," and
televiewing have little in common with the harsh world of
struggle whence sprang primitive man. What is common is the
habit of platitudinous garrulousness, dubbed by Malinowski
"phatic communion," for to quote Malinowski, "among un-
civilised peoples, speech scarcely serves as a vehicle of profound
reflective thought; early man, like the modern savage, probably
talked a lot but had little to say."

Our own choice of words follows certain trends: new words
are coined, new meanings learned and adapted. The words we
use vary with our age, our interests, the play of the environment
upon us and hackneyed phrases, to be used or avoided, come
and go. Pronunciation varies to a greater extent than spelling,
but it is principally in the choice of words that we reflect the
personality of our age. National characteristics may be reflected
in, or reflect, the rigidity and flexibility of its grammer. The
world of entertainment, modern music, recent inventions all
provide the pattern of change apparent in similes and metaphors:
"not so much . . . more a," "with it," "in the mood," "jazzed up,"
"sputnik," "teleflash," "landslide" (as applied to politics), "black-
out" (as applied to medicine) are words bearing the hallmark
of our times. Some, indeed, already appear dated, but others are

used with little realization of their recent origins. Max Muller commented that all words expressive of immaterial conceptions are derived from metaphors. It applies to ourselves, it applies to the society in which we live and it has applied over the centuries.

The comparative study of language shows plangent yet surprising changes as we look backwards into history. Modern English and modern Chinese contain a higher proportion of monosyllables than other tongues and modern English is renown for its grammatical flexibility. Leopald Stein pays the English language a particular compliment in this respect: "The more advanced a language is, the more developed is its power of expressing abstract or general ideas. Everywhere language has first achieved expressions for the concrete and special. English syntactical construction is most free in the arrangement of its constituents. So great is this flexibility that relations can be expressed in much greater variety and precision than in other languages, e.g., the difference between 'I am being extravagant' and 'I am extravagant.' "

There is little difficulty in recognizing modern words from the Saxon and Norman stem words but in declension and grammatical construction the words have undergone enormous simplification. Particularly in other bygone languages transmutations of prefixes and suffixes prevail and involve adverbs and adjectives as well as nouns and verbs. The literature of the past was frequently subjected to the strict rules of prosody; sagas and legends took on a complex poetic form, the rhythm or measure was determined by rhyme and by a succession or grouping or feet or stresses and marked by a definite recurrence of ictus.

The vocabulary of these earlier languages contained fewer words with abstract meaning and many specific concrete words. Among backward peoples today a similar state of affairs often exists. Thus the aborigines of Tasmania had a name for each variety of gumtree and wattle tree, etc. but they had no equivalent for the expression "a tree." The Mohicans have words for cutting various objects but none to convey "cutting" simply. And the Zulus have such words as "red cow," "white cow," "brown cow," but none for the cow in general. Otto Jespersen has noticed a curious discrepancy in this respect. Anglo-Saxon literature possessed a great number of words connected with the sea which were selected primarily with regard to the alliterative needs of the poesy. He concluded that this situation had arisen, because the nation which had been seafaring turned to other livelihoods while reminiscences of the sea still lingered in the imagination. Jespersen found another unique feature of the English language, namely the existence, sometimes for centuries, of the two slightly differing forms of the same word: one the original English form and the other the Scandinavian, e.g., no—nay; rear—raise; from—fro; shirt—skirt; edge—egg. He deduced from this that the rapid succession of invaders—Anglos, Saxons, Jutes, Norsemen and Danes—forced to fraternize, trade and rule over others whose language was sufficiently close to be understood without much difficulty, resulted in a sacrifice of the niceties of grammar and greater flexibility of form. The intelligibility of each tongue came to depend almost entirely upon vocabulary, and so the linguistic simplicity of English grammar—but not alas of English spelling—resulted from the diversity of its settlers who could not be bothered with the minutiae of the language for such accuracy was quite unnecessary for understanding.

Semantic trends are, by and large, best illustrated not by recourse to literature, but from the comparative study of extant languages and their standing in the gradings of civilization. Trends are seen in the proportion of primitive phonetic sounds—clicks, syllabic reiteration and nasalized consonants, and in consonant substitution or elision. Languages vary in the proportion of words devoted to abstract ideas, in vocabulary size and vocabulary shape. The language of the most primitive peoples is usually slight in vocabulary but shackled by the sheer complexity of its own grammar. Diamond has analyzed the changes in vocabulary shape, finding in primitive society a very high proportion of verbs—50 per cent as opposed to 10 per cent in present-day English. As the vocabulary increases he finds that the proportion of nouns (which are often derived from verbs) increases and later the number of adjectives enlarges. In all cases he claimed that the majority of "roots" began as verbs.

We do not know the form of language of early man. Many centuries have elapsed since he first came on earth. Did he share the emphasis which primitive people extant today place on superstition and mystery? Is there a parallel with the way in which reading and writing were the prerequisite of the learned man to be found in the case of speech? It may have been that all but the simplest words and commands were the prerogatives of the elders and witch-doctors of the tribe, or the means of converse between the priests and their gods.

Chapter 6

THE ESSENTIAL REQUIREMENTS
FOR SPEECH

"You may think that there are other more important differences between you and an ape, such as being able to speak, and make machines, and know right from wrong, and say your prayers, and other little matters of that kind; but that is only child's fancy, my dear. Nothing is to be depended upon but the great hippopotamus test. If you have a hippopotamus major in your brain, you are no ape."

CHARLES KINGSLEY, *The Water Babies*

THE MECHANISTIC BASIS of speech, its transmission and reception, does not depend on the possession of anything structurally new. Old structures have been adapted for the purpose of speech and most, if not all of these structures, retain something of their earlier function. Nature is rarely wasteful in its use of structure. To find out at what level of evolution human speech took its origin, it is necessary to analyze the fundamental essentials for speech, to see which structures are vital and which subsidiary in the production and reception of speech, and to trace the adaptive changes that have occurred to make speech possible. Speech needs to be examined in all its aspects: formulation, expression, articulation, hearing and understanding. The story is one of increasing differentiation, specialization, integration and interconnection of structure.

Speech Production

It is simplest to begin with an analysis of structure by firstly studying the production of speech. Words must be shaped by articulation and made audible by phonation. A variety of methods are found within the animal kingdom, the more unusual of which are used by insectivora, but almost all higher verte-

49

brates prefer a bellows and reed system involving the lungs and laryngeal sphincter. Sound is produced by "phonation"— the release of controlled bursts of air by the larynx. This phonated air provides the requisite volume for the sound. To be converted into speech, the phonated breath is modified by movement of the muscles of articulation and given resonance by passage through the pharynx, nasal and buccal cavities.

The lungs, which provide the bellows part of the mechanism, are evolved from the piscine swimbladder. The change is first evident in the adaptation of the lung fish to terrestrial survival through gaseous exchange with the atmosphere. The protective sphincter enabled the lung fish to return to its aquatic habitat.

We owe our present knowledge of the comparative anatomy of the respiratory passages to the outstanding contributions of Sir Victor Negus. The stages of evolution he adumbrated, and his principal suppositions, are still accepted with a minimum of criticism. He found that the laryngeal sphincter of the lung fish was relatively crude. It was not until a much later stage of evolution was reached, when animals first took to an arboreal habitat, that a more delicate control over this sphincter appears. A monkey swinging from branch to branch relies upon his arms to grip firmly and support the whole weight of his body. The unyielding grip must be matched by the secure connection of the shoulder girdle to the rest of the body. The arms must be fastened securely to the animal's trunk to obtain full purchase from the muscles. The muscles fixing the shoulder girdle take origin from the rib cage and, if the ribs are to form a stable base from which to contract the muscles, the ribs must also be held firm relative to the rest of the body. Theoretically, this might have been achieved by more powerful abdominal muscles fixing the ribs to the pelvic girdle but to do so would require an enormous expenditure of muscular energy. A strong laryngeal sphincter closing to contain a fixed amount of air within the lungs achieves exactly the same effect with great economy of effort.

Among the arboreal monkeys—lemurs, gibbons, and chimpanzees—the inlet valve is particularly effective as a valve able to exclude all but a definite volume of air. By comparison, although the control is still highly developed, the inlet valve of those terrestrial anthropoids, who have abandoned life in the trees and do not demand such power in the arms, is structurally less efficient. In man, for example, this valve, named the *inferior thyro-artenoid fold,* is more rounded and lacks the sharp edge of the valve of lemurs or chimpanzees.

In discussing the function of any anatomical structure relative to speech, one may ask a general question whether, or in what way, ablation of that structure affects speech. This provides a crude approach to the physiology of an organ but as our knowledge of speech in man is so much a function of our knowledge of the patho-physiology of human speech, it does provide an important addition to the central theme. For instance, the larynx is not indispensible with regard to speech. In certain individuals esophageal speech is possible. Air is taken into the stomach or into the lower part of the esophagus and, by careful release, can be turned into rasping but distinguishable sounds. Such esophageal speech may be acquired by adults who have had their larynx removed (the operation of laryngectomy) for malignancy. Those who develop useful speech and can still continue their former occupations are, in most instances, patients who had previously been good (and were perhaps trained) speakers. But many patients lack the ability to train themselves for this form of communication, and it is doubtful whether a laryngectomized infant could ever acquire intelligible speech.

Animals in an arboreal habitat depend relatively more on vision and less on their sense of smell than do terrestrial animals. Their sense of smell is degenerate and is no longer relied upon for survival. It is therefore no longer necessary to maintain contact between the epiglottis and the soft palate. The result of a gap between the epiglottis and the soft palate is that laryngeal sound may escape, in part or almost entirely, by way of the oral cavity. Buccal speech is louder, clearer, and possesses more tone than nasal speech. A wider range of articulation is obtained by changes in the positions of the lips, teeth and tongue.

Not all human speech is buccal, even today. The individuality of the voice depends in high measure upon the resonances obtained in the nasal antra and sinuses. Throughout the ages of man there has been a process of increasing denasalization. Among aboriginal people such as the Senoi nose-flutes are used instead of lip-flutes but few of us could play even the crudest tune upon such instruments.

In what is reputedly the best English (Queen's English) only three consonant sounds *m*, *n*, and *ng*, are formed by complete closure of the mouth and the passage of air through the nose. There are no nasalized vowels. In French, nasalized vowels are still used—*an, en, in, on,* and *un;* and vowel nasalization is also found in certain American accents, in faulty pronunciation, with palatal defects, and in common French, Portugese, Dutch and German mispronunciations of English. When these speakers use nasalized sounds, the soft palate is but partially raised and fails to touch the back of the pharynx. With this lower palatal position a mixed nasal and buccal sound is produced, and, experimentally, it has been shown that slight nasalization of vowels does in fact occur in English when they precede nasal consonants. However, the amount of nasalization found with Queen's English is not sufficient to give the vowels a characteristic nasal timbre.

Speech is often blurred by gross defects of articulation deformities of the hard palate, harelip or paralysis of the soft palate, but it is still possible. It is even possible after removal of the tongue—a most curious fact for, as Stein has emphasized, the German Zunge, Greek glossa, Latin lingua, French langue, Czech jazyk, English Mother tongue, all denote the fleshy organ in the mouth which is used for talking. A language without lingual sounds, devoid of *t, d, n, r, s, sh,* can easily be imagined and speech pathology has provided instances wherein individuals have lost the greater part of the root of the tongue through disease and yet have been able to speak intelligibly.

The shape of the mouth also affects articulation. With increasing use of the hands for grappling and tool-using, the teeth have no longer to fulfill a protective function. Anything especially tough can be broken into smaller pieces by implements or torn asunder in the hands. There is no longer the need for a strong and bulky jaw musculature. The two halves of the mandible can form a broader arc allowing greater space and freer movement of the tongue. Further roominess is obtained by transposition of the bony brace buttressing the junction of the two sides of the mandible from the inner aspects of the jaw, where it formed the simian self, to the outer aspect where it adds to the prominence of the human chin. Thirdly, additional muscles controlling the movement and position of the tongue take advantage of the space afforded by the broadening of the buccal cavity and lessened jaw musculature. Some of these arise from the genial tubercles, bony prominences found only in man, which have developed by the backward projection of spikes of bone from the interior of the chin region. Their size is unrelated to speech capacity—a fact commented upon by Professor E. A. Hooton, when explaining that there is a sex variation in their size and shape. The genial tubercles are smaller in women than in men.

The structural anatomy of the air passages undoubtedly affects the character of one's speech. It renders the acquisition of human speech, and even the mimicking of human speech, by animals much more difficult. It also determines within the human species the relative facility with which different races can produce different sounds. Some of these changes are genetically determined; thus, for example, Darlington correlated the ease of pronunciation of the *th* phoneme in Europe with the dominance of ABO blood groups; and, more fundamentally, we have the postulation of Schewidetzky, suggesting a blood-group relationship between races using certain primitive sounds and anthropoids also employing these crude grunts and clicks.

The functional as well as the structural anatomy of articulation has undergone change. The muscles of the pharynx and larynx, are bilaterally innervated. If the brain stem is damaged on only one side, as might occur with a blood clot, the articulation of speech might be impaired for a few days but thereafter there would be compensatory changes and a return to normal speech. This fact is equally true in man as it is in lower animals. Both the minutiae of motor control and the kinesthetic feedback from the articulatory muscles must have undergone a fine development. This fine development ably adapted to fulfill speech needs was grafted on the mechanisms primarily designed for the vital functions of respiration, mastication and deglutition. The development of the additional skill of articulation culminating in human speech has evolved late in the course of evolution and provides additional support for the proposition that human speech is a unique human achievement.

Man differs from the other primates in one essential respect: his ability to understand speech and to formulate the expression of speech also depends upon the control of the speech centers which are asymmetrically situated, that is to say control of speech can be permanently damaged in man by a unilateral cerebral lesion. His ability to cry or yell will be unaffected, his control over the muscles of articulation will be unimpaired, his hearing of words will remain intact but he will be rendered aphasic by damage to the dominant hemisphere containing the essential speech centers.

The Hearing and Understanding of Speech

The human ear is formed around a small neurectodermal remnant of the lateral line—the organ of balance in fishes. This same neurectodermal remnant becomes in the dolphin the sonar or echo-receptor used to determine the distance and direction of objects and perhaps even to discern their shape and composition. In man, the neurectodermal auditory plates become converted into auditory vesicles continuous with the ductus endolymphaticus of the vestibular apparatus. The whole audi-

SPEECH REQUIREMENTS

1. *Phonation and Articulation*
   Development of larynx.
   Denasalization of speech.
   Changes in mouth: i   teeth;
          ii   width of buccal cavity;
          iii loss of simian ridge;
          iv   presence of genial tubercles.

2. *Hearing*
   Brain stem startle reflexes.
   Cortical representation of hearing.
   Development of association areas.
   Feedback mechanisms.

3. *Brain Development*
   Increase in brain size: "prolonged fetalization."
   "Cellular" changes.
   Asymmetry of function.
   Cerebral integration and association.

tory cavity is formed as a recess between the first and third visceral arches and comprises the second visceral arch and its pouch with the addition of elements from the first and third arches and pouches. The organ of hearing, including the auditory nerve, cochlea, middle and external ear, is completed by the end of the perinatal period. Babies can hear sound from the day of birth and it is even possible that the fetus responds to sound from the thirteenth week of intrauterine life onwards.

Since the work of R. T. Beatty, *Hearing in Man and Animals* (1932), little has been published on the comparative anatomy of the ear and still less on its functional aspects. In Beatty's opinion, the function of hearing in the lower mammals is largely protective. Sounds are the main warnings of impending danger. The faintest sound must be heard, localized and acted upon before there is time for thought. In contrast to the ability to hear, the ability to discriminate between sounds is but slowly acquired by infants. Although the baby hears from the first moment, he does not consistently react to sound until the second month; if suddenly startled he will, on most occasions, respond with a movement of the whole body; but on other occasions his response will be limited to a blink. At four months he acquires the ability to localize the direction of a noise and to modulate his voice when cooing; and in the ensuing months he derives pleasure from the repetition of babbled sounds. Thus, the reaction to sounds is initially immature in comparison with other mammalian species, and further changes in auditory discrimination and the discrimination of pitch take place up to about eight years of age.

We know very little about the audiometric range of higher apes and for this reason the audiometric range of early man must remain a matter for conjecture. When did man achieve the auditory skill necessary for speech discrimination? The gross auditory ranges of the higher terrestrial mammals differ only fractionally from species to species, but such differences are important. Many animals, for example the dog and bat, have an auditory range greater than that of man, particularly in the upper register. Ability to hear a bat's screech or a dog whistle is just within the range of a boy, but is usually lost in adults.

If there were differences between the auditory range of modern and early man one would anticipate a difference in character of speech. If the range of early man were only a fraction less than that of modern man, it is possible, *vis a vis* children with high-tone deafness, that the higher frequency sounds, *s*, *sh*, and *th* for example, would be distorted and the vowel sounds deprived of their distinctive upper harmonies. In such a case the speech of early man would have been comprised of flat, unmusical grunts, totally different from that inherent in the Festal hypothesis of speech. I am indebted to Professor Harold Schuknecht of Harvard Medical School for information concerning the determination by behavioural conditioning techniques of the auditory ranges of several types of monkey. By these methods, Dr. Shiro Fujita, in Detroit, has obtained the threshold sensitivity curves of the Cynomologous, Rhesus and Squirrel Monkeys. These show very little difference in their auditory range from that of man and although the ape has not been studied by either electrophysiological or behavioural methods, it can be reasonably assumed that its range was also similar to that of man. It is highly unlikely that either the ape or early man had a frequency response higher than that of modern man. However, although the audiometric range might not be very different from our own, it remains possible that the functional speech range over which sounds could be clearly recognized and remembered would be somewhat less. Or alternatively, that though sounds might be remembered for their pitch over a wide range they would be less likely to be remembered for their content.

The startle reflex whereby a sudden noise may cause an adult or child to jump may be a more highly-developed reaction in certain animals than it is in man. Finer sounds, often of higher pitch than those discernable by man, will cause the animal to react—to tense a hare feeding quietly, or cause a cat to stop, look and listen, and then prepare to scuttle from sight. Beatty described these reflexes as being controlled and co-ordinated by centers in the brain stem, of which the inferior colliculus is the highest. Sound analysis in the lower mammals, was, so he thought, subserved by fibers ending in the inferior colliculus, for very few of the fibers from the cochlea are projected to the cortex, and in lower animals the cortex has little to do with hearing.

Primates show a much more elaborate cultivation of the acoustic territories of the cortex. The human "hears" at a cortical level. In the cortex, hearing becomes understanding. Parts of the cortex are primarily concerned with the reception of auditory fibers and these are linked to adjacent auditory association areas among which are included the sensory speech areas of Wernicke.

With the lengthened intracranial pathways for hearing and the elaboration of cortical speech reception, it may reasonably be assumed that organic as opposed to psychologically determined deafness is possible in the presence of a normally functioning inner ear. Worster-Drought, in 1957, made a distinction between inability to hear due to "central deafness" caused by lesions affecting the transmission of sound within the brain, and inability to comprehend which he termed "congenital auditory imperception," probably due to lesions of the interpretative cortex. Usually the two phrases "central deafness" and "auditory imperception" are regarded as synonymous and are said to result from a disorder of function above the auditory nuclei in the brain stem.

Patients with word deafness do exist but authenticated cases are few by comparison with those in which the diagnosis is presumed to be present. There is undoubtedly a difference between the ability to hear noise and to interpret it in the understanding of speech, but the nerve fibers for sound recognition and sound analysis are one and the same, possibly up to cortical level where the finer analysis of words and the relation of understanding to thought occurs. At this level the speaker will become aware of his own voice as he speaks, and will modulate his voice, round his sentences and select his words with care, mindful of the impact they are making.

It is wrong to talk of speech analysis purely in terms of sound analysis, for word recognition is, to a large extent, an interpretation of a received speech image. D. B. Fry and others have shown that 70 per cent of words may be guessed from their content, the facial expression, lip movements, part-hearing of the words and the emotional presence of the speaker. The same is true when a deaf person speechreads. Even the most skillful lipreader needs to guess nine out of ten words. This is made far easier if something of each sound can be heard, i.e., if the maximum is made of the rudimentary residual hearing still left. Thus, whether words are recognized by hearing alone, as over a telephone, lipreading alone, or the combination of lipreading and fragmented hearing of some sound resonances, the act of word recognition is a complex integrative cortical activity and this requires not merely intact cranial nerve pathways and a degree of brain stem integration but also the presence of a highly-developed cerebral cortex.

Brain Size and Development

Numerous attempts have been made to correlate brain size and shape with the ability to speak. Phrenologists have claimed that such a correlation can be extended to the skull itself. It has been said that a brain must reach a weight of 950 gm or a capacity of 1,000 cc before it can serve the ordinary needs of human existence and before it can become the seat of even a low level of human intelligence. This statement would exclude the likelihood of speech in a chimpanzee (brain weight 350 gm), a gorilla (400 gm), a twelve-month infant (900 gm), Pithecanthropus (650 gm), with Pekin man and the Neanderthal man (900 to 950 gm) just on the borderland of speech. Lilly,

BRAIN WEIGHT AND HUMAN SPEECH
(STATEMENT OF LILLY'S THEORY)

SPEECH UNLIKELY BELOW 400 G. → CHIMPANZEE 350 G

MIMICRY POSSIBLE 400-900 G → 4 MO. INFANT
PITHECANTHROPUS 650 G

SPEECH POSSIBLE ABOVE 900 G → 14 MO. INFANT
NEANDERTHALER 950 G

perhaps the foremost advocate of absolute brain weight and speech capacity, adds that between 400 and 900 gm mimicry of adult vocalization is possible. This statement is reminiscent of that of Wallace that "speech is acquired by children solely by imitation . . . Speech was formed and evolved, not by children, but by men and women who felt the need for a communication other than by gesture alone."

Lenneberg, on the other hand, claims to have found the beginnings of language developed in microcephalics. This development peters out for their intelligence advancement shows a negatively accelerating exponential, levelling off or slowing down with a very prolonged period during which few further words are acquired. But a start is made by both microcephalics and nanocephalic dwarfs. (The brain size of a nanocephalic dawf, a pin head, never increases above that of a newborn child.) Lenneberg postulated from data based upon a follow-up

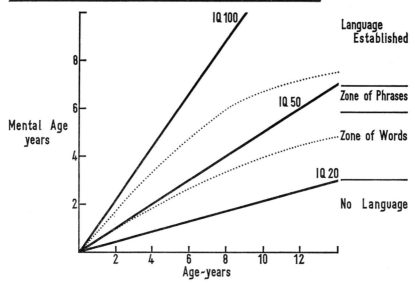

RELATIONSHIP between SPEECH DEVELOPMENT and INTELLIGENCE.

...... = empirically determined decay rates.

U.C.H.M.S. 2193/213~65. V.K.A.

study of sixty-one mongoloid and twenty-three children with other types of retarding disease that speech is a genetically determined prerequisite of humans and that an intelligence quotient as low as 20 is adequate for a human to acquire the use of a few words, at an IQ of 30 to acquire a few phrases and above 50 to establish language.

He does make one proviso that with retardates secondary psychological factors do affect speech. "The onset of speech is an extremely regular phenomenon appearing at a certain time in the child's physical development and following in all children the same general "strategy" from the time they begin to the period at which they have mastered the art of speaking . . . The mentally retarded child makes a normal or an increased amount of sound. Vocalizations are quantitatively those heard among normal children. The only difference is the age of appearance. Mutism or highly bizarre sound production are definitely not characteristic of mental retardation."

But, to return to Lilly's theory: the skull capacity of Neanderthal man was, in some instances, larger than the modern average; but whereas the modern skull-vault is high, Neanderthal man had a low but very wide skull. A. Koestler *in Darkness at Noon* paints the Neanderthal as uncouth and bound to the earth, trampling gloomily through the woods, banging around with clubs, devouring raw meat, transgressing every law and tradition of the jungle, without animal dignity. This was the Neanderthal man as seen by the nineteenth century, a hideous ferocious brute. But there is evidence that he buried his dead with offerings and behaved with altruism to his fellows.

Some 30,000 years ago Cro-Magnon man existed with a brain capacity of 1,600 cc. But the outstanding example of a large-brained ancestor is Boskop man, predecessor of the present day Bushman. Boskop man was more richly endowed with mass of brain than any other human type. He had the appearance, according to Sir Arthur Keith, which philosophers have speculated as representing man of the future, with great heads, small jaws and diminutive bodies. But he presumably had not the wit to save himself from extinction.

Boskop man, Cro-Magnon man and—we must presume from

his elaborate rituals, Neanderthal man—all made use of speech, but it would be fruitless, though interesting, to speculate upon what their speech may have consisted. There is conflicting evidence as whether Pithecanthropus possessed speech. Stein supposed him capable of impulsive gestures, some of them productive of sounds and noises correlated to the fundamental emotions of love, hunger and fear. He presumed that such reactions were mainly controlled by subcortical layers which, in view of the relatively small brain, "must be assumed to have been dominant."

The time scale for human evolution has been revised many times. Leakey estimates homo habilis—the first able, handy, mentally skilled man—to be 2,000,000 years old, Australopithecine man 1,000,000 years old and Java man and Pekin man 400,000 and 600,000 years old respectively. In 1918, F. Wood Jones had reckoned that Proconsul africanus was 20,000,000 years old. But from Cesare Emiliani's studies of the chalk deposits by means of the oxygen eighteen method (published in 1956) we are nowadays inclined to accept a much foreshortened time scale. The onset of the first glaciation in Europe, the Gunz glaciation, was probably no earlier than about 600,000 years ago. By this reckoning the last ice-age, the Wurm glaciation, receded about 20,000 years ago and between these periods the ice sheets waxed and waned in 50,000- to 60,000-year cycles. This new chronology would place the early man-apes (Australopithecines) at about 600,000 years ago, the Pithecanthropus in the middle of the Pleistocene epoch 500,000 years ago, Neanderthal and Mouster-

EARLY MAN

PLEISTOCENE		
600,000 BC	AUSTRALOPETHICINES (MAN APES)	Ist. GLACIATION (GUNZ)
500,000 BC	PITHECANTHROPUS (JAVA MAN. PEKIN MAN)	
MIDDLE PALEOLITHIC		ICE AGES
80,000 BC	NEANDERTHAL MAN	
UPPER PALEOLITHIC		
50,000 BC	CRO-MAGNON MAN	LAST GLACIATION (WURM)
40,000 BC	MODERN MAN	

ian man 80,000 years ago and Cro-Magnon and modern man as arising in the Palaeolithic period 40,000 to 50,000 years ago. Compared with the slower evolution of the mammals and reptiles, the enlargement of the cerebral hemispheres of man by 50 per cent seems to have taken place, speaking geologically as Edinger remarked "within an instant," and without having been accompanied by any major increase in body size.

The brain of man, unlike that of any other animal, trebles in size in the first year of life. At birth it is no bigger than that of a gorilla, but in the prolonged period of infancy the brain tissue retains its embryonic potentiality for change and growth. The brain of homo sapiens is outstanding by reason of its general fissural complexity, the relatively high ratio of brain weight and the presence of certain regional or localized elaborations.

It is only possible to examine brain shape and to gauge the brain weight of early man by examination of the skull-vaults of his fossilized remains. One may study the disposition of the cranial venous sinuses where they have indented the inner surface of the vault. The torcula Herophili, sulcus lunatus, fossa parietalis, frontal eminence and occipital fossae may be recognized from these grooves. The sulcus lunatus appears as an indentation of the inner table of the skull in Pithecanthropus. In the majority of specimens the sulcus appears to be more conspicuous on the left side and the occipital fossae are unequal in size and depth. These findings do not, on closer inspection, collate with either unilateral cerebral dominance or with the creatures' handedness.

The fossa parietalis is seen bilaterally in the skulls of pre-historic man. This may be regarded as a specific hominid feature, Parietal and frontal eminences occur in the cranial casts of Pithecanthropus; the parietal prominences are more obvious still in the Neanderthal man and show a further advance in modern man.

Human speech differs from non-hominid vocalization in that a unilateral cerebral lesion may be sufficient to damage it ir-revocably. This fact was first recognized by the Spanish physician Dax, in 1836, but it was not until 1877 that he acclaimed his finding in print with the title "Lesions of the left half of the brain associated with forgetfulness of the signs of thought." Broca has since designated a pre-Rolandic area of the left hemisphere as the motor speech center and Wernicke has found in the temporo-parietal cortex a center for receptive speech, or understanding. Others have contributed in other areas, though, in fact, there is no constant, discrete, speech center either for reception or expression. Yet others have descended into myeloarchitectonics connecting certain cortical cells, in certain cortical layers, in particular areas of the cortex, with speech. Kleist in 1962 subdivided the "speech cortex" still further. He localizes the appreciation of noises and specific characteristics of sounds which have significance for speech to the second transverse gyrus; the appreciation of tones to the first transverse gyrus; the comprehension and monitoring of phoneme sequences to the posterior part of the first temporal convolution; the comprehension of sentences to the superior part of that region; and the comprehension of the meanings of words to the subregio audio-dorsalis on the second temporal convolution. Such exact anatomical relationships based upon autopsy material are an anathema to most neurologists and neurophysiologists today. Their attitude to cerebral localization is much more plastic. It is very difficult to produce a deficit in a specific fraction of total speech without also affecting the more amorphous, essential inner speech through which reception is allied to formulation.

Hemisphere Dominance

Traditionally, handedness, or hand preference, is linked with speech, but the nature of this kinship has yet to be clearly determined. Most of the people of the modern world are right-handed but there are islands and races wherein the majority of the population are left-handed. In other racial groups left-handedness is seen as a minority trait; for example between 5 and 10 per cent of the population of Britain or America would consider themselves to be left-handed—the trait being twice as common in males as in females. Left-handed individuals, for the most part, owe their handedness to a familial trait but for some sinistrality is an acquired feature, the result of brain injury. Incomplete right dominance ambidextrality and crossed laterality may be the result of a brain lesion or of a genetic factor, or—and this is the reason most commonly cited—the result of physiological immaturity of brain function.

The limbs are innervated by nerve fibers which cross within the nervous system; thus the right hand is controlled by the left cerebral hemisphere and vice versa. The impulses which the hand sends to the brain cross to the left side. The movements of the hand are directed from the left half of the brain. The arrangement of nerve fibers alters, dependent up which segment of the brain or spinal cord is examined. In the region of the internal capsule, deep in the cerebral hemispheres, the fibers relaying to the hand are separated from the nerves to the face for the fibers to the rest of the upper limb are interposed between them. However, the pattern of representation on the cortex is as though the hand were held to the mouth and were partaking in the expression of speech. Is this symbolic of an innate relationship of speech to gesture? As Charlotte Woolf says: "The hand, in which the sense of touch is most acute, has developed in one way as an affiliation of the mouth which in animals still serves as an organ of prehension as well as of eating. In man, the former capacity has shifted to the hand; but the ancient link between mouth and hand is still mirrored in brain representation."

The higher centers for speech—areas which may be ablated in animals without impairing vocalization but which if traumatized in man render him aphasic—are sited in one or another cerebral hemisphere. The best-known cortical area for speech (Broca's area) lies close to that part of the motor cortex subserving movement of the hand. In right-handed people, the left cerebral hemisphere practically always subserves speech but in left-handed people, except in certain genetically determined cases, the laterality of the speech center is not as clearly demarcated. Hecaen and Angelergues, in 1962, detailed the degree of vulnerability of speech to various lesions in man:

In left-handed people, whatever the side of the lesion, the expressive disorders occur significantly more often than they do when there are left-sided lesions in right-handed people.

Disturbances of understanding occur very rarely in left-handed people with either right or left-sided lesions. They occur significantly more often in right-handed people with lesions of the left cerebral hemisphere.

The frequency of amnesia, aphasia and agraphia is similar in right or left-handed people with left-sided lesions.

Alexia (inability to read) occurs significantly more often in left-handed people with left-sided lesions than with right-handed people wtih similar lesions.

Finally, one must stress the fact that these aphasic disturbances in left-handed people are always more transitory than in right-handed people.

These statements may appear somewhat confusing to people unaware of the complexity of the subject of cerebral dominance. The subject may be more easily understood from the practical aspect. How does a neurosurgeon seek to discover which is the dominant side of the brain before embarking on an elective operation? In a right-handed person, unless there is evidence of crossed laterality, he may safely assume that the speech center is on the left side. But in a left-handed person he must resort to Wada's sodium amytal test. A soporific drug, such as sodium amytal, is injected into one common carotid artery in a dosage which will produce transient weakness in the limbs of the opposite side of the body without causing the patient to fall asleep. In the meantime the patient is asked questions requiring a non-stereotyped reply and thereby any transient dysphasia is discovered. Even if injection into the right common carotid causes transient dysphasia, the surgeon should also check the effects of injection of the other carotid vessel. He may then have to decide which injection caused the greater disruption of speech.

The type of assault upon the cortex—thrombosis, haemorrhage, atrophy or tumor—rarely matters; the important factors are the site and the extent of the lesion. The age of the patient is also important for the brains of children are more plastic; compensatory processes are more able to make good a deficit. For this reason, acquired aphasia is rare in childhood. The function of speech may be successfully transferred to the opposite, undamaged, hemisphere. A child below five years may still be able to speak although his dominant hemisphere has been removed. Evidence of less severe cerebral damage in childhood may be obtained by the electroencephalogram, asymmetrical limb growth or the finding that the child, alone among all his relatives, is left-handed.

There are other forms of acquired hand preference. It was a common practice at one time to teach left-handed school children to write with their right hand (converted sinistrality). Social etiquette frequently demands that left-handed people act as though they were righthanded. They are expected to hold their knife in their right hand. In Arab countries the left hand is used for toilet purposes and is therefore regarded as unclean. The Kaffir will scald the left hand of a child who appears to be using that hand preferentially. In one way or another social codes, pressures or cultural laws decree that children and adults act as though they were right-handed.

Laterality preference may be examined in a number of ways. Preferences are to be found for the eye used in sighting an object, for the foot used to kick hard and accurately, the way one crosses one's legs, folds one's arms, uses nail-files, scissors, or dusters, and writes and draws. It would seem from the studies of Blau and many others that the more specialized the activity, the higher the degree of right-sided development; whereas the simpler functions approach a fifty-fifty chance division. The hand preference for writing is somewhere between 90-10 and 95-5.

None of these facts, enlarging upon the complexities of lateralization, detract from the statement that there is a relationship between handedness and speech laterality. It might be equally true to say that there is a relationship between footedness or foot preference and speech laterality, but the fineness of function performed by the hand contrasts sharply with the crudity of action of the feet. It is entirely reasonable to stress handedness and ignore footedness. It is possible that eye preference arose *pari passu* with speech. Man and the apes presumably acquired binocular vision because their ancestors took to the trees. In an arboreal environment where the sense of smell is of lessened importance, greater reliance is placed upon vision.

In binocular vision, on eye tends to become the guiding eye and the other eye then converges to subtend the same visual field. No two eyes are perfectly poised in equilibrium and to achieve convergence there must always be some overt, if miniscule, muscular adjustment made, sometimes by the oculomotor musculature of one eye, sometimes of the other, but rarely with full parity between the two eyes. Although the anthropoids do not show asymmetry of the occipital lobes this ocular dysequilibrium could provide the foundation of cortical and, hence, cerebral, asymmetry.

This argument has appeared in one form or another countless times. Gould in 1908 claimed that one eye had better vision than the other and hence it is easier for the hand closer to the better eye to coordinate with it in performing motor activity. Parson in 1924 introduced a visual test for sighting or fixation. He showed that in this function we are all of necessity one-eyed, otherwise we get a double image. This eye is not necessarily more perfect visually than the other eye but it fixes the "visual line" and the finer musculature coordinates are guided by the visual line of the preferred eye. For "sighting" there has to be an alignment of three points: the center of the macula, the point of regard and the target. But a straight forward relationship between the sighting eye and the cerebral hemispheres does not exist. The field of vision of one cerebral hemisphere is continuous with, but does not overlap, the field of vision relevant to the other hemisphere, neither is the field of vision of one dominant to that of the other, and for tasks requiring accommodation, judging distances or dimensions, and for purposes of movement, the two hemispheres and the two eyes work together. As Brain has said: the truth is that sighting is a quite exceptional visual performance. It is a kind of pointing—we point a gun—and the primary activity in pointing belongs to the hand. In practice, it is extremely difficult to be sure that any test for sighting does not involve other factors such as hand preference.

Animals do show some degree of laterality preference but this preference is less sharply demarcated than in man. Archeological studies do not prove conclusively at what stage in man's evolution a definite hand preference is first seen. Christian

Thomsen in Copenhagen and Sir John Lubbock in England divided the artefacts of the Stone Age into the Paleolithic Stone Age of rough stone implements (600,000 to 12,000 BC) and the Neolithic Stone Age after 12,000 BC. Hand-shape and manipulability, and probably also hand preference may have evolved in adaptation to the use of tools. The more refined polished instruments do provide evidence in their manufacture of hand preference but some of the cruder paleolithic tools could have been fashioned by a simian hand. If the neolithic tools are examined it will be seen that almost half show a preference in the their manufacture for the left hand, but modern archeologists are highly skeptical of this interpretation. It is extremely difficult to infer the handedness of the user from either the shape or the flaking of a flint implement. The first definite evidence of the hand preference of primitive man is shown in the late paleolithic drawings found in the caves at Lascaux. Many of these drawings show men holding weapons in their right hands.

The standard phases of archeological culture—the Neolithic Stone Age, the Bronze Age and the Iron Age—cannot be used without ambiguity except with reference to Western Europe. The phases presuppose the availability of mineral deposits and malleable stone. Little is known of the social history of early man elsewhere. It is wrong to deny the existence of a particular civilization because of the paucity of its relics. Theophile Gautier's immortal lines,

> *Oui, l'oeuvre sort plus belle*
> *D'une forme au travaile*
> *Rebelle*
> *Vers, marbre, onyx, email,-*

conceal a fallacy.

To regard an East African tribe as prestone age because they use no implements and are hunters and food gatherers is ridiculous. Nor can we argue that because such people show definite hand preferences and have a large vocabulary that the acquisition of manual skills neither dictated hand preference nor contributed to the evolution of speech. We know not where the cradle of civilization lay. We do not know from whence the aboriginal peoples of today migrated. Have they secondarily adapted to their present habitat? Were they driven from a more favoured habitat? We cannot tell.

Our conclusions from the archeological evidence must be somewhat limited. Early man did possess some degree of hand preference and left-handedness very probably occurred more frequently than today.

The determination of laterality does not depend entirely upon inherent factors. It is much more plastic, reflecting in part, as Blau has suggested, psychological and social deviations which are, Blau says, often founded upon negativistic personality traits. There is a functional interaction between the individual and his environment. Psychological and cultural influences decide which cerebral hemisphere is to dominate. However, one factor which may be cited as suggestive of an inherited determination of laterality is the hair whorl. In right-handed people it develops in a clockwise direction. In left-handed people it rotates in an anticlockwise direction. This difference in the hair whorl may be most clearly seen in mirror-image twins where a mirror-image pattern of the hair whorl is coupled with left-handedness. Such an attribute as the hair whorl is unlikely to be an acquired characteristic but more careful studies of its relation to handedness and other aspects of laterality are required.

The existence of twins is a boon to human geneticists. Dahlberg in 1926 studied the handedness of 124 pairs of uniovular twins. In only six pairs were both left-handed, in the majority (89 pairs) both were right-handed and in twenty-nine pairs one twin was left and the other right-handed. In the binovular twins studied by Newman, Freeman, and Holzinger, in 1937, left-handedness was four times less common than among uniovular twins, but this figure nevertheless is nearly twice as frequent as in the general population. Situs inversus (when the heart lies in the right side of the chest and the abdominal viscera are transposed) is not associated with left-handedness.

Chamberlain found in the population at large that where both parents were right-handed only 2.1 per cent of their offspring were left-handed; but where either or both parents were left-handed the incidence of left-handedness in the children rose to 17.34 per cent. In families with both parents left-handed, 46 per cent of the children were also left-handed. He supposed from this information that left-handedness was inherited as a Mendelian recessive gene. But Brain, in his classical review of handedness and speech, does not fully concur with this supposition. If, he says, a Mendelian recessive gene was the sole factor in determining handedness, then one would expect all the off-spring and not merely half the offspring of left-handed parents to be left-handed. A modifying factor must be present to explain the difference in sex incidence, and an environmental or learning factor, such as Blau postulates, must also be operative.

The evidence to date most fully concords with Brain's view. Handedness is in part determined by inherited factors and in part the result of adaptation to the environment; these factors may become alloyed with each other during the process of maturation. The intermixture of heredity and environmental factors early in life may succeed without psychological disturbance; but when environmental factors arise at a later stage their fusion with inherited factors is liable to be incomplete and profoundly disturbing.

Cerebral dominance does not mean that one hemisphere is larger than its opposite and dominance does not always imply a more lowly role for the non-dominant side. In such tasks as spatial orientation the so-called non-dominant hemisphere may dominate. In practically every task where the dominant side has an active role the non-dominant side performs an equally important supportive function. In writing, the dominant hand moves the pen, the non-dominant hand steadies the paper. In kicking, the dominant foot strikes the ball, the non-dominant foot carries the weight of the body and thereby maintains the body in an upright, balanced posture. The principal advances of the human brain over the non-hominid brain is in its integration. The integrative use of the nervous system above the purely reflex level is acquired in infancy and childhood. Intuitive action may be supposed to represent that level of integration in which hereditary factors predominate and reasoned action where acquired "wisdom" predominates over ingrained influences. Speech and laterality develop oncologically with the maturation of integrative mechanisms. Speech is unlikely to have developed simply as a by-product of handedness. Unless chance has led to the association of lateral dominance and speech in the same hemisphere. It is more probable, as Brain has said, that it was the appearance of a motor speech center in the left hemisphere in man that made that the dominant hemisphere, and the right hand the dominant hand, in contrast to the apes in which right and left-handedness develop with equal facility.

Toolmaking and Speech

The later Neanderthal finds are highly significant to the archeologist and to those who will learn from archeological research. The Mousterian finds not only include a Neanderthal man but relics of Ice Age beasts such as the woolly mammoth. The evidence of that era shows quite definitely that at that time, man had already made tremendous advances. He was able to shape stone weapons by polishing them, without, however, giving up the practice of chipping. He could domesticate animals, cultivate cereals and fruit trees, weave linen, manufacture pottery, erect megalithic monuments and there was definite evidence of religious beliefs and a funerary cult. This being so it is incredible that Swedenborg and others would have us believe that man lacked speech right through the Old and New Stone Ages and did not develop it until the Bronze Age. Gestural language may have been elaborated by the unemployed hand but in the creative tasks of the neolithic period the hands were busied in action at just those times when primitive man needed to communicate most urgently.

Toolmaking may have begun well before the neolithic era. De Vore, in *Horizons of Anthropology* (1965) presents evidence from the reduction in the size of the teeth as compared with those of non-hominid primates that the first man-apes, the Australopithecines, approximately 600,000 BC rarely made use of their prehensile teeth and jaws and must therefore have long since used tools to replace the canine teeth in hunting and defence. They most probably used unshaped stones to break or dig for it may be assumed that though they hunted they were still primarily vegetarian food gatherers.

Toolmaking may be linked with speech in either of two ways. Firstly, it provides the need for speech (Barber)—a man cannot readily communicate with his hands and work with them simultaneously—and he will need to communicate precisely because he is using tools. He may need assistance or he may be instructing another in his art. And secondly, toolmaking provides evidence of sufficient advance in integrative ability for man to have been able to develop speech (Miller).

There are other theories linking speech with inability to communicate manually. Diamond claims that the earliest words would be calls for assistance when hunting or fighting. He suggests that these might have been short explicatives like "break," "crush" or "pull." At night some audible form of communication would have been necessary to maintain contact. Paget similarly suggests that when eating man's gregarious nature urges him to communicate with the others foregathered to partake of the feast. The smacking of lips and other noises of appreciation develop into a means of communication for his hands are probably grasping the food, tearing it or carrying it to his mouth.

Yet others have suggested that the blind or partially sighted were the first to communicate by voice. Those who have travelled in the poorer countries of the world will testify to the menace of blindness. Cairo has been called the City of the Blind, and in vast areas of Ethiopia, Arabia, India, and China, blindness afflicts a large proportion of the population. Most of the blindness is caused through viral disease such as trachoma, but infection, sepsis, trauma and senile changes account for much visual disability. Man is the only animal among whom the handicapped can continue to fulfill a role within the community. Traditionally the lame became the blacksmiths or carpenters, the weak became the scribes and the blind became renown for their poetry or their memory. The partially sighted could from the earliest days have been of some help to the community if they could converse with them. They could be the experienced elder, for they would be able, without being in a position to lead themselves, to be of immense value to the leader in scheming hunting sorties or remembering how past difficulties were surmounted. If one member of the community feels the importance of having an audible means of communication, something more meaningful than grunts or groans, then the advantages may quickly become apparent to others within the group.

Toolmaking must also be linked with the use of the brain for what may be called symbolic thought. If a man pauses to fashion a tool before any sort of action, he is introducing the concept of preparedness or flexible postponement. To quote G. A. Miller, "It is not enough to say that homo erectus could coordinate his hands well enough to shape a stone tool. It is equally important to recognize that toolmaking is only a component of a much larger, hierarchically organized plan of action that could be formulated and carried through only by a highly intelligent playful creature, only by a creature, that is, who was capable of flexible postponement."

Symbolic thought, the planning of action, and the shaping of tools—itself a plan of action—are greatly facilitated by the use of speech. It is possible that toolmaking and speech, though they both provide evidence of a development of symbolic and integrated thought—developed independently. But it is more reasonable to construe that some intimate connection must have existed between these two evolutionary innovations and that (if we may once again quote G. A. Miller) "human speech is the most important tool of all."

Chapter 7

THE LESSONS OF CHILDHOOD SPEECH

It is by trial and error guided by the ear that the baby learns all articulated processes. It proceeds like the violinist who tunes his instrument.

J. FROMENT

"Le mot n'est pas une unite, mais un complexus"
CHARCOT. LA LANGUE INTERIEUR

P IERRE BOULLE, author of *The Bridge on the River Kwai*, deserves to be as well known as the author of many other intelligent novels, such as his space-fictional *Monkey Planet*. Scientists have managed to teach the higher apes—chimpanzees, gorillas and orangutans—to speak. By mimicry the apes are able to perpetuate this speech faculty throughout their species and then succeed in turning the tables on man. The book is, in essence, a satirical diatribe against animal experimentation whether vivisectional or behavioural. The apes sieze command by rendering man mute. Man, thus, becomes the experimental animal; some are subjected to ablative experiments and others are watched and analyzed as they attempt to reach food with a stick. Civilization, dominated by the apes, remains almost static. Its existence is dependent on learning through mimicry, and only the chimpanzee is found to possess any vestige of originality.

This novel serves to stress the distinction between the level of brain development required for mimicry and the much higher requirement for other forms of learning. Children learn at first by mimicry but as their brain trebles in size so do they become capable of initiation of language. Pierre Boulle's novel serves as a reminder of Wallace's dictum that speech was formed and evolved not by children but by men and women who felt the need to speak. There is need to express caution in the inter-

74

pretation of speech evolution in childhood and not presuppose a parallelism between ontogenetic and phylogenetic linguistic development.

The next point to be recognized is the relative precariousness of speech development. This may at first appear a somewhat paradoxical remark in the light of Lenneberg's claim that speech is an innate human function, its inception independent of intelligence, prematurity, sight or environmental influences. Lenneberg's findings are only acceptable within a limited context. Speech development is precarious in that the faculty is lost altogether, if a start has not been made before about the seventh year of life, and because the progression from babbling to speech is dependent on a variety of reflex mechanisms, environmental, organic and psychological.

That there is a critical or sensitive period for language-learning up to seven but most highly developed in the early months can be ascertained by several means. The most fascinating evidence in this respect comes from the study of feral (wild) children.

Only Romulus and Remus appear to have survived their early vulpine upbringing free from adverse effects; with the others the tale is very, very different. The diary of the Rev. J. A. L. Singh provides a full account of the return of the wolf children of Midnapore to civilization on Wednesday, November 24th, 1920, and their subsequent development. The elder child Kamala was presumed to be about eight years of age when rescued and the younger Amala one and a half years old. The account of these children has been popularized by A. Gesell's *Wolf Child and Human Child* written twenty years later, but it is the earlier diary of the Reverend Singh which is most informative. It was believed that Kamala had lived among the wolves for seven years. Two years after being rescued she spoke only two words and seven years later spoke a mere forty-five words.

Other animals have featured in the upbringing of feral children—gazelles, gorillas, bears, sheep, leopards, pigs, etc. There appears to be no essential difference between children nurtured by animals and those left to fend for themselves in a wild or deprived state like Kasper Hauser who was cast into a dungeon when aged three and emerged in 1838, fourteen years later, with a spoken vocabulary of only a few words.

Linnaeus in the eighteenth century drew up a list of nine examples of feral man of varying authenticity. The earliest was Hessian the wolf boy of 1344. He considered that they shared three important characteristics, *tetrapus, mutus et hirsutus,* and on this basis sought to classify them as a subspecies of man, homo sapiens ferus. Whether they can justifiably be regarded as a subspecies is a little doubtful, the Rev. J. A. L. Singh delayed reporting the fact that he had two wolf children at his mission as they were girls and to publicize their feral origin might have hampered their marriage prospects!

More information on feral children is given in Professor R. M. Zingg's review, published in 1939, as the second half of the Rev. Singh's account of Amala and Kamala, *Wolf Children and Feral Man.* Professor Zingg showed that of thirty-five children, only three showed any substantial recovery after their early isolation. Linnaeus's supposition that feral man is necessarily hirsute has not been found to be true, he quite commonly walked on all fours, but that he should be mute and devoid of all recognizable language is almost invariable. Since 1939 there have been other feral children: the wolf child Ramu who was discovered near Lucknow in 1954, a seven-year-old child shut up in a hen-house in Northern Ireland, 1956, two gazelle boys found in Lebanon in 1955, and a gorilla boy aged about fourteen, captured in Northern Persia in 1961. It is characteristic of these children, denied the formative years for speech in a human milieu, that save for a few animal grunts, they were unable to speak in any tongue, remembered or invented.

These then are the dramatic examples. There are many, more numerous and less-spectacular examples. Throughout the ages mutism or dumbness has been considered practically synonomous with deafness in early life and it is, alas, also true that hearing children, for some reason presumed deaf, have been treated as such, neglected and are unassisted in the development of language. Lastly there are a few rare neurological conditions which may lead to failure to develop language They include word deafness and articulatory apraxias.

The prevalance of mutism, inability to speak in a recognizable voice, among children denied the faculty of hearing still exists today. Modern audiological and educational techniques have enabled most deaf children properly taught to acquire some useful speech but it is not invariably the case. If correct teaching is initiated from an early age and if the child is intelligent the chances of continued mutism are diminished, but it is possible even for these children to fail to develop proper language. One can truly declare that congenitally deaf children do not speak unless especially taught.

If the child is normally hearing at first and then at the age of four or five becomes deaf, as from meningitis, it will tend to forget that vocabulary which it already possessed or, alternatively, may develop gross distortions in articulation. Such children invariably require help to sustain their pronunciation and vocabulary. A similar situation does not appertain to adults who become deafened, speech intelligibility is not affected though there may be changes in voice intensity. Adults with a conductive hearing loss are inclined to reduce the volume of their voice, whereas those with a perceptive form of deafness may increase their voice and unwittingly shout at all and sundry.

A more intimate relationship between hearing and speech in children is suggested by the condition of high-tone deafness. These children are incapable of hearing the upper range of speech sounds. Unfortunately, as Whetnall and Fry point out, this interference is not merely a matter of attenuation of the high frequencies, but in addition there may be considerable distortion of these frequency bands and hence intelligibility loss cannot be compensated readily. The higher consonant phonemes, *s, sh, th, r,* and *l,* are lost as are the upper resonance frequencies of the vowel sounds, resulting in an unintelligible dyslalic speech characterized by the substitution and omisson of recognizable speech sounds.

Not only do the first words suffer in adverse circumstances but so too does the evolution of babbling. Analysis of babbling is always extremely difficult. Individual variation within the limits of normality is considerable. Babbling is best studied ontogenetically. Tape recordings made at monthly or bimonthly

LANGUAGE DIFFICULTIES OF THE DEAF.

No reflex encouragement....................."Babbling" dries up.

Syllabic difficulties...........................High notes distorted or not heard.

Inadequate "Inner language."

Concepts ~ comprehension difficulties..Abstract words, ethics etc..

Interests lack stimulus.

Speech offensive to others...................Harsh and monotonous.

U.C.H.M.S. 2193/211 ~ 65.   V.K.A.

intervals are compared phonetically. Whereas one child may babble incessantly, another child, for no apparent reason, may scarcely babble at all. The linear study of recordings of one individual is by no means fool-proof. An observer who calls on a family and takes a short recording of the child's babbling, then does not see the child again till six weeks later, may obtain an entirely false impression. The child's babbling may be influenced by the immediate state of the child. Is he well on that day? Has he just eaten? Had his bowels opened? or Had he just awakened after a longish sleep? To circumvent these difficulties, K. P. Murphy and his co-workers rely on the mother to take recordings over the course of a few days whenever the child appears to be babbling particularly well. They have to their credit over 6,000 recordings of deaf and hearing babes selected from a population at risk.

Murphy distinguishes three types of deaf response: firstly, those with central deafness appear to have an imperfect pattern of sound production from birth; secondly, those with very profound peripheral deafness may display a misleadingly normal range of sound inflection; they differ from normally hearing infants in that their early vocalizations are possibly immature for their age and this impression of immaturity is heightened as the babbling stage is reached at about nine months, in fact true babbling does not occur; in the third group, representing all but the severely affected, vocalization up to the stage of babbling may give a similar impression of immaturity; even so, the child does babble eventually but inflecton remains limited in range and speech infantilisms persist. In this group, sometime between nine and twelve months speech development peters out, vocal quality is lost, consonants disappear, the vowels become progressively more guttural and the end state of mutism is reached. It is possible to alter this scheme of events provided the early vocalizations are reinforced by parental encouragement and repetition so that sounds develop with the normal symbolic quality.

Preliminary investigations of the speech development of children with normal hearing brought up in a deaf environment, with, for example, both parents being profoundly deaf, suggest that, in the majority of instances, the babbling stages proceed unhampered but in a few instances there is a danger that babbling may dry up. By and large, speech development in these children proceeds more smoothly than in neglected children or institutionalized children. It is apparent that the babbling stage is normally reinforced by a number of reflex mechanisms and these will be evaluated later in the discussion of the whole process of babbling.

There is a singular fascination in the study of speech evolution in childhood. The development of the spoken word from the prelinguistic utterances of infancy and the very fact that it can be influenced by environmental factors which may be studied individually, suffice to suggest that here is a source of data applicable to the origin of human speech which we can ill afford to ignore.

Considerable mystique surrounded the early interpretation of infant speech, the birth cries were particularly appealing in this respect. How better than that they should provide a recognition of original sin. The birth cries were rendered into Latin. Male infants were thought to make a sound "o-ah" with the second syllable weakening unintelligibly. This was said to represent *"O Adam cur peccavisti"*—Oh Adam why hast thou sinned?

Mystic was replaced by a more scientific approach directed by psychologists and academic linguists. They tackled their subject with a Teutonic determination. First came the "splitters" and infant speech was docketed into numerous stages and substages. To these, interpretations were given, some implanted Freudian terms depicting the ego being built upon the id. The five-month vocalizations were reported as those of displeasure on withdrawal of a coveted object, at six months of pleasure and at seven months—a climactic satisfaction in the attainment of an objective (Gesell, 1929). Equally lyrically, M. M. Lewis referred to babbling as a form of art, presenting the characteristics of language with an esthetic intention. In addition to the "splitters" and "interpreters" there came the "lumpers." These tended to gather together dissimilar data from multitudinous sources. Some of these authorities, notably MacCarthy and Stein, have made praiseworthy attempts to rationalize this approach; but whether splitter, interpreter or lumper, the primarily linguistic approach, however scientific in conception, fails to overcome its essentially unbiological treatment of a preeminently biological subject. Nonetheless, it would be very wrong to treat their work with the contempt which appears to be so popular today.

There is a valid reason why we should break away from the interpretations placed upon infant speech by classical psychologists. Unless we do so we will fail to obtain a holistic view. For them language became more enthralling than the nativity and growth of the whole child. For example, Revesz lists eighteen definitions of speech or language based on philological criteria. Unfortunately none of these are helpful in anticipating the changes from the vocalizations of the newborn to those of a fluent adult. It is not helpful for our purposes to use a definition which understands language when present in its totality: the ordered sequence of words, the system of conventional signs voluntarily produced, the total stock of man's perceptions and conceptions. At this stage we need a dynamic definition which suggests the steps whereby speech is built up from prelinguistic vocalizations in infants. Perhaps Morley has provided the best definition for pediatric purposes. "Speech is an integrated function involving the reception of words by the ear or the eye, their interpretation and synthesis as language within the brain,* and the expression of this language response in further spoken or written words. Experience and memory, at each stage in the sensori- motor mechanism of speech, make smooth the workings of a crude but rapidly maturing system." We would do well to analyze this more fully, taking in turn each of the three main steps: reception, interpretation and expression.

The organ of hearing, like that of smell but unlike that of sight, cannot be switched on and off at will. The way in which a human localizes sounds is somewhat different from that of most mammals. The pinna cannot be moved so as to find the direction from which a noise comes and localization is quite ineffective before the fourth post-natal month. However, we all know that in a crowded gathering certain sounds or voices, not necessarily any louder than the general hubbub about us, suddenly attracts our attention. We then are able to listen to them by some form of selection. This selection does not depend on the ear. Selection, shifting and decoding occurs at a higher level. The level which if faulty can give rise to word deafness. Listening, to an extent we cannot easily estimate, depends on the establishment of auditory rapport with the speaker. Quite possibly, other factors such as smiles, gestures, atmosphere, the appearance of concentration while listening, enhance or catalyze this part of the act of communication.

We know little of the interpretative stage—the introspective analysis or inner language. It is almost invariably affected by any process causing loss of speech faculty; a purely motor or expressive disorder, or a purely sensory disorder are rare occurrences. For inner language, thought, emotion, perception spatial and temporal factors, intelligence and drive are all interlinked

---

* It is remarkable how few definitions take note of this inner language originally adumbrated by Hughlings Jackson.

and synthesized.

The act of outgoing communication, which we have termed expression, is more easily divided into stages. This fact is to some extent responsible for the undue emphasis placed upon speech making and the relative neglect of speech reception in the etiology of language. The first stage of expression is the initiation of speech, the desire and decision to express oneself, the idea to be expressed and its formulation into words, the right choice of words and the semantic and syntactical compilation of the prospective utterance. Still within the brain, the prospective utterance must be transmitted into precise kinesthetic images for phonation and articulation. Neuromuscular impulses are released which correspond with these kinesthetic stimuli. This is the act of speaking and the words, the volume and the inflections are modulated during the act of speaking by a continuous auditory and kinesthetic feedback. For most speakers an instinctive feeling of audience rapport, usually affected in the main by visual and auditory stimuli, provides a further modulating feedback device. Sir Alexander Ewing who was principally concerned with the way by which deaf children learn to talk, speaks of vision as the third cybernetic factor. It is wrong to regard this factor as applicable only to the deaf.

Speech Reception

(A) *Hearing*: The newborn child responses to sound are entirely reflex. He possesses an innate ability to make little grunting, throaty noises. He listens to sound. He begins to discriminate between them, startled by some, calmed by others, but as yet there is no indication that heard sounds affect his own utterances.

From about five months a definite change occurs. Although the vocalizations are still not syllabic, it becomes possible to distinguish between the vocalizations of, say, a Japanese and an American babe. The vocalizations take on inflections dependent on the language of the parent; thus German umlaut sounds or French guttural "r's" are distinctly heard. There is an increase in the quantity and quality of vocalization varying with the situation presented to him, whether toys, food, etc. He appears to enjoy his vocalizations, to reduplicate them and play upon them. This is the stage of babbling. Babbling is stimulated or motivated by his surroundings and then reinforced by his own auditory feedback and by the response it evokes from others. This is a form of crude but effective mimicry which is to provide the foundation for speech. Once the ear-to-voice link is established for a variety of sounds, babbling and later speech proceed as inexact mimicry. The child responds to the sound he has just heard with the nearest similar ear-to-voice link that he has been able to seize upon—thus for doll he may say da. Throughout the whole process of speech-learning, listening precedes speaking. It soon becomes evident, weeks or even a month or two ahead, that the child understands a word before he actually executes that word himself. To use Gesell's semantic spoonerism, the child learns to listen and listens to learn, only later does the word become part of his expressive vocabulary. The babe held in its mother's arms is essentially a passive-receptive vehicle to its mother's influences and not least for communication.

The child must rely upon heard speech for his correct articulation. The inflections of vowel sounds are imparted early in life and are less-readily altered than the consonants later on. If a severely deaf person speaks with a clear accent his deafness can only have been acquired after he had begun to speak. Templin found that the ordinary, unhandicapped child takes about eight years to learn to speak with correct articulation. If there is a hearing loss these auditory errors will continue. Girls show less tendency to persistent errors in articulation than boys and, according to the Ewings, children of lower socio-economic status take about one year longer to attain essentially adult articulation than those in the upper socio-economic group. The loudness, pitch and quality of children's voices commonly attain the standards of social acceptability at about four and a half years of age. In a nonspecific handicap such as cerebral palsy, speech is delayed on average between two and four years. The earlier linguistic school is at one with modern thought in emphasizing that mature human speech may evoke attempts at speech from an infant. It was thought that a relatively silent or listening stage was interspersed between babbling and the utterance of words at about the fifteenth to eighteenth month. This silent phase is denied by later observers. It is quite distinct from the two stages of preparedness: the period of readiness to listen covering the whole of the first year (Fry and Whetnall, 1954) and the period of readiness to speak from the twelfth to the eighteenth month (Stinchfield and Young, 1938).

(B) *Kinesthetic Factors (Bastian 1897)*: As we have seen, the initiation of words is based upon kinesthetic memory: the calling forth of varied patterns of neuromuscular responses. Thereafter, the control of speech production is chiefly modulated and sustained by the auditory feedback mechanism; but this control decreases in importance once speech has developed into a habit. The voice of a deafened adult may lose its tone yet the acquired speaking ability remains. A hearing child learns words almost entirely through hearing. If he becomes deaf his memory for acquired words does not vanish: they have remained in part as kinesthetic memory—a less stable form of memory, perhaps, but one which if stimulated, is capable of useful development. This "muscular memory" as Dr. Mary Sheridan has dubbed it, must normally be subconsciously exercised in the process of speech, in fact Burt has suggested that we normally recall our consonants by muscular memory. A child may be consciously taught to correct a defect in articulation by reference to the relative position of his tongue or lips when speaking and this corrected articulation then unconsciously sinks into his further pronunciation.

In 1944, Weddell, Feinstein and Prattle recorded electromyographic potentials from the intrinsic laryngeal muscles of seven human subjects. The amplitude and duration of the di- and tri- phasic impulses are of the same order of magnitude as in the external ocular muscles and in the muscles innervated by the facial nerve. Since then, several other studies of the muscles of articulation, both during phonation and at other times have been made of the action potential patterns. Activity is still observed during quiet respiration. The activity is of low amplitude and the single motor unit potentials cannot be distinguished from each other. Exceptionally, in a few subjects only, is there no activity during breathholding or quiet respiration in the crico-thyroid, vocal and thryo-arytenoid but even in these subjects a resting electrical activity of 200 to 500 pv is still present in the absence of phonation in the posterior crico-arytenoid muscle.

Various increases in activity occur with speaking, whispering or so-called silent speech. Silent reading is often subvocal with a simultaneous utilization of silent movements of the lips and other articulatory muscles during the act of scanning a page of text. Truly silent reading, without the intervention of whispers or movements of the lips or glottis, is the hallmark of the experienced and highly-skilled reader who is scanning a text wherein both vocabulary and subject matter lie well within his competence. It is a common experience, when we catch someone unaware in a pensive mood or about to write, to notice that his passive attitude fails to hide silent lip-movements and perhaps even apparently meaningless movements of his fingers. Human electromyographic studies have shown that during the processes of reading, thinking or writing, amplitude of the action potentials from the larynx and the muscles of articulation is raised above the resting level. Thus, before we dismiss the kinesthetic feedback mechanism of speech, we can note that both visual and electrical observations, in hearing as well as in deaf individuals, underlie the importance of all the so-called and much neglected kinesthetic memory. Here we have new evidence in support of Johannesson's hypothesis of speech-gesture relationships.

(C) *Visual Factors*: The visual factors in speech learning, while not essential to good speech, is nonetheless important. Once a child becomes a fluent reader it may constitute the most important means by which new words are acquired and the child's vocabulary increased. Then visual memory for a word may be added to auditory and kinesthetic memory. An adult may be said to have a photographic memory or an essentially visual memory. In the preceeding stage, vision is an aid to speech: to reinforce babbling, to attain correct pronunciation, most especially in a foreign language, to grasp the meaning of an unknown or difficult word, and in the case of the deaf, as the sole means of understanding speech.

Most of the vocalizations of babes under six months are reflex responses to discomfort or occur as part of bodily movement. Sometimes at this tender age the human voice can conjure forth sounds from the child, but not invariably so. It has been observed, countless times, that responses to an adult voice occur most readily if the adult first catches the child's eye and then smiles during the act of speaking. When the child begins to use syllables or words significance is implanted to its new found skill by what the child sees. The child says 'da' and the mother says 'doll' and presents the child with a doll. The child says "bi," the mother says "biscuit" and hands the child a biscuit. If later the child hears a new word, he will look up and expect to grasp the meaning of the word from what he sees. And this habit will remain with him throughout life.

Dr. Mary Sheridan, from a study of a hundred blind children between eleven and thirteen years of age has drawn attention to the manner by which a child learns to imitate a wordshape by watching his mother's lips and consequently corrects defects in the pronunciation of consonants. She showed that despite their highly-trained auditory attention, blind children showed a far higher percentage of defects in articulation than did ordinary school children. In fact, 45 per cent of blind children compared with 53 per cent of mentally defective and 30 per cent of five-year-old elementary school children made articulation faults. The defects they showed were principally those of "s," "th" and "r." In other words, they showed the usual tendency of all children to confuse these sounds, but for a longer period and to a more marked degree. It was Dr. Sheridan's belief that not only are these sounds the most difficult for the child to distinguish by ear, but also that vision normally plays a definite part in learning to distinguish between all the finer consonants. Deaf and partially hearing children not unnaturally show the most numerous and severe speech defects, but among these the mispronunciation of *"th"* as *"f"* was never seen in isolation, although this is the most common single defect of all among the blind and retarded. She concludes that this must be because the child with impaired hearing very soon learns the necessity of watching the speaker's lips.

The need for speech in our civilization is inescapable, and without adequate means of communication with others the individual so affected must always be at a disadvantage. This is the situation in which the deaf find themselves. By signs they can communicate rapidly among themselves but the uninitiated can rarely follow more than a few of their gestures and is at an even greater loss when trying to reply in kind. Besides this, many of the signs are crudely and slovenly formed. People may learn the elements of finger spelling in a few minutes, but only through constant practice can they keep up with a rapid finger speller. A person taught by finger spelling may gain a good knowledge of vocabulary, grammar, reading and writing, but will remain mute, rather like a 140-word-per-minute typist sent to Coventry by her mates. Because communication is so difficult without speech, the deaf have been taught to speak often at the expense of other aspects of their education. They have been taught to watch others speak, to lipread—or speechread as many of them prefer to call it—and to watch themselves speak. This is the oral method, called by its detractors the German method. More recently, with the advent of hearing aids, it has been realized that all but a few deaf people possess a little utilizable "residual hearing" and this discovery has been incorporated as an educational method, the aural method, in the teaching of speaking and lipreading.

Lipreading is an inexact means of following speech. The Royal National Institute for the Deaf has a pamphlet on conversation with the deaf which emphasizes that about nine out of every ten words have to be guessed by even the finest lipreader in the world. At all times this calls for concentration and strain on the part of the reader and with certain people, lipreading may be a sheer impossibility. Children are taught to lipread as far as possible, at the automatic level, to appreciate the meanings of words or sentences rather than to identify consonant or vowel sounds. Use is made of games and pictures to assist learning. With older children and adults three simultaneous lines of approach are used:

(1) Eye training in watching and discriminating movements;
(2) Conscious recognition, or the practice of recognizing

and associating lip movements with meaning, and

(3) Direct lipreading—this is used from the beginning with very simple material.

Lipreading is enormously assisted if through the use of hearing aids some speech sounds are heard, and in addition the lower resonance frequencies of other sounds are heard at the same time. If some sounds are appreciated, the chance exists that the person will speak with a reasonable tone devoid of additional extraneous noises which distress the listener.

Other Related Factors: Before passing on to an organismic or holistic concept of speech development, we must first consider other factors. For in addition to those already discussed, organic disease, intelligence, psychological factors, prematurity, delayed maturation, and the cultural level and attitudes of the parents all influence language development.

Brain damage may lead to subnormal intelligence, it may cripple with or without causing dysphasia. Lesions involving the motor pathways, whether they are pyramidal, extrapyramidal or cerebellar, will affect the muscles of phonation and articulation. Speech in cerebral palsy is commonly delayed. It may be very difficult to distinguish between the dysarthria which is part of an obvious or persisting minimal cerebral palsy, an isolated dysarthria, dyslalia and articulatory dyspraxia. With the dysarthria of cerebral palsy, there will be alterations in the muscle tone and widespread neuromuscular dysfunction. Involuntary athetoid movements may supervene. Low intelligence may or may not be associated with delay in the processes of language acquisition. The stages will be the same as for normal individuals. At first there will be little difference in progress, but somewhere on the ladder, perhaps at the stage when the child has just begun to walk, progress will show a negatively accelerating exponential, and level off or slow down with little evidence of further advance within a very prolonged period of time. A child who has learned to name objects may stick at this stage with little further addition to his vocabulary. If the IQ is below 30 he may be able to use words but not phrases. He may however be able to parrot a sentence without understanding either its meaning or its syntax. A child with an IQ above 50 should be able to acquire normal language and clarity. In practice, as Lenneberg so frequently found, mental retardation is often complicated by the secondary development of psychological problems caused by conditions created by the primary disease. The mentally retarded child makes a normal or an increased amount of sound. Vocalizations are qualitatively those heard among normal children. The only difference is the age of appearance. Mutism or highly bizarre sound production are definitely not characteristic of mental retardation.

Prematurity may result in delay in the early vocalization. The child's sounds are initially feeble. Prematurity can coexist with inherited abnormalities, a high incidence of birth trauma and lowered intelligence: all these factors may influence speech. Kastein and Fowler (1959) studied the language and speech development of sixty-six survivors of premature birth who had reached two years. Thirty-seven of these had retarded development of language, with or without "organicity" while thirteen with adequate or advanced language development also showed signs of "organicity" (evidence of damage to the central nervous system).

Delay in language development is often a cause of parental worry; the parent becomes suspicious that any delay in a child reaching his milestones signifies mental retardation. Once the voice mechanisms come under voluntary control they become susceptible to emotional factors. Furthermore, no neuromuscular mechanism can function truly until the neural mechanism controlling it has reached an adequate state of "preparedness" or maturation. Illingworth (1960) rightly emphasizes that "no amount of practice can make a child sit, walk, talk or acquire other skills until his nervous system is ready for it."

Late talking is not uncommon. Bastian, in 1897, described an epileptic child, aged nearly five years, whom the parents had taken to various specialists because of dumbness. Then, an accident happened to one of his favourite toys, whereupon he suddenly exclaimed "what a pity," though he had never previous spoken a single word. The same words could not be repeated, nor others spoken, not withstanding all entreaties, for a period of two weeks. Thereafter, the boy progressed rapidly, and speedily became most talkative. "When seen by me he spoke in an ordinary manner without the least sign of impediment or defect."

Maturation is a word used in more than one sense. When we talk of maturation of a reflex such as the Babinski reflex, we mean that the reflex has changed from the child type to the adult type and this change correlated well with the laying down of myelin around the axons of the larger cortico-spinal fibers. Insofar as it is possible for use to rationalize, we can say that for this reflex maturation appears to require the myelination of the main cortico-spinal tracts. About the time that these fibers become myelinated the normal child begins to walk, thus myelination of the cortico-spinal fibers suggests a preparedness for walking. The child has matured sufficiently to begin walking. Difficulty with this term arises when its meaning is extended to apply to other activities. Wepman has pointed out that the brain is at its most receptive for learning at a time when myelin is being laid down. The fibers of the psychic portions of the motor, somaesthetic, visual and auditory cortices acquire their sheaths later than do the cortico-spinal fibers and the association areas become myelinated last of all. The whole process of myelination is not completed until the eighteenth year or perhaps even later. The rate of myelination is genetically predetermined. The term maturation but not myelination may be used synonomously with functional development. The developing nervous system is, to some extent, plastic. Specialized development is influenced by external stimulation and by an internal striving to satisfy the needs of the total organism. Wepman's proposition is that the speed of maturation can be determined by function and that the individual in attempting new tasks adapts the neural structure to accommodate the more complex organization required of it. Thus, those children whose learning is easiest along the auditory modality (audile) will bring to fruition those language functions dependent on audition earlier than will the children who are "visile." Conversely, the "visile" child may be delayed in starting to talk and in acquiring accuracy in speech, but does much better when he approaches that part of the learning of language which calls for visual skill.

The attitude of the parents may help or hamper speech. Parents may neglect a child for psychopathic reasons; but their neglect of the child may not be vicious. They may suspect deafness and cease talking to the infant because they feel it is useless. It sometimes happens that a particularly garruluous woman is so intent on gossiping with other adults that she neglects to address herself to the child. An alternative state of affairs may be that the parents are always anticipating the child's needs before it asks, speech is consequently delayed; then at a later stage, pampering and soppiness lead to a continuation of baby talk and a failure to correct the faults of diction that go with it. The cultural attainments of the parents will affect the size of the vocabulary which the child acquires, its diction and the grammatical quality of its speech. More especially the intelligent parent will influence the child's speech through encouragement and interest.

This, so far, has been a factorial study of childhood speech. Our interest has lain in the analysis of why and how each factor, taken separately, can influence speech. We have looked at this superficially, avoided as much as possible a deep phonetic study and we have made no attempt at quantitative investigation of these factors. A detailed investigation of the speech of children has been made in 1957, by M. E. Morley.

The Organismic Approach

Hermann, writing on word-blindness, coined the adage, "not the eyes but the brain learns to read." This might with profit be adapted for our own purposes, "not the ear but the brain learns speech." It directs our attention to the essential, which cannot in any circumstances be circumvented. In a deaf man the eyes can listen. In a deaf-blind person, such as Helen Keller, the hands can listen. The ears are not essential. The tongue, the palate, the vocal cords, all take part in normal speaking but any of these can be taken away and yet with training that person can still talk. The brain learns, listens, elaborates and initiates speech. Perception is attained by a synthesis of sensory appreciation. Learning is by synesthesia. It increases, *pari passu*, as the perception of its ever-enlarging environment increases. To Watts, the worlds of touch, sight and sound are at first quite separate but language is associated with the assimilation of these worlds within the child's body image.

Credit for the origination of this holistic approach deservedly belongs to Goldstein (1948). His "organismic" approach to language development was founded in opposition to the earlier atomistic theories. Every individual speech performance, he considered, is understandable only from the aspect of its relation to the function of the total organism in its endeavor to realize itself.

This theory not only competes with the earlier atomistic theories but rests in fundamental contradistinction to the contact theory of Revesz. To Revesz the utterances of early man and today's child are produced actively. At first solely for the exchange of feeling and to convey the need for contact. And this plays an active preparatory role producing the need for purposive communication into which it ultimately develops. He believes that speech evolves from the cry to the call to the word.

The writings of M. M. Lewis support and antedate Revesz' theory. Language, he says, is essentially a form of action—social action. The child, perhaps innately—certainly very early in life, has manipulative and declarative needs. However, this innate urge for self-expression may be a fallacy. The child has a natural gift for mimicry. Also, at each stage, the child listens and learns; there is then a delay when he appears to store up or cogitate on the newly acquired information, and then he can express himself. A child may be moulded within his environment, he is not an originator. He learns about his environment, and then learns to adapt to that environment. Therefore, it is more reasonable to concentrate upon the receptive phases and the build up of perception than upon the subsequent adaptive expression.

The child's first world is comprised of mouth and nipple. His next world includes a fuller but by no means a complete awareness of his body as part of a mother-child continuum. The continuum becomes a communication dependent upon the closeness of direct body contact and the empathic relationship of mother and child. It may be remembered that from the beginning he may receive sensory stimuli from his separate sensory worlds which are extraneous to his focussed attention. To these he reacts by a whole body response. A subtotal response implies that a particular stimulus has been recognized, at any rate, in part, by the child's awakening conscious. Consciousness is comprised of the child's focussed attention and his bodily awareness, primitive id and primitive ego. His first vocalizations are almost certainly outside consciousness.

The term *higher sensory perception* denotes those recognized sensory patterns which are probably within the bounds of consciousness or accessible to it. The developing brain is particularly pliant to change; this is especially so in the first two years of life. Compensation for a sensory fault at a lower level can best be made by the sensorium at this time. Between three and four years of age the child is most suspectible to habilitative measures to surmount a handicap or a defect of perception. With increasing delay in the correction of a deficit the natural pliancy is lost, training is less easy and emotional factors are liable to supervene. Thus speech should be learned as early as possible.

There is another important spatial factor, the concept of which owes much to Dr. Mary Sheridan, it may be referred to as "mother distance." When the child is held close he can only listen, observe and receive. He is, in Rose Spiegel's phrase, a passive receptive vehicle. His sensory appreciation is, at first, poorly developed. The very closeness of the mother allows him the greatest chance of observing her expressions. Other distractions are eliminated. When she speaks, the proximity of her voice enables him to hear her loudly and clearly. His gaze will naturally be focussed on her at a time in life when localization of sound is still imperfect and he will read from her expression and actions something of the meaning of the sounds he hears. This meaning becomes established by repetition.

It may be presumed that at about this time he is becoming aware of his own vocalizations. He can hear them; he can feel them in his mouth, his throat and his lungs. He tries to equate his vocalizations with those of his mother. How he next proceeds may be illustrated by the simile of an older child playing the guessing game of hot, warm and cold. If his guess is a good one he will be told it is hot; if bad, cold, and so forth. The infant attempts to copy the mother. Besides his own appreciation of the noise he will observe the expression of his mother. She may repeat the sound. His sound follows closely on hers and she augments it be repetition. He will later be tempted to try his sound *de novo*. If it matches the situation, it will be indicated by her expression. She will, almost as a Pavlovian reflex, repeat it. Her response may be stored in his memory and the beginnings of a word-situation, word-meaning stratum erected.

As the child grows up, he will crawl and later he will toddle. The mother-distance is increased. He will not always be looking at her. Even if within earshot, he will first have to localize where the sound is coming from and secondly, whether her voice is directed at him. He no longer receives the close, loud, direct voice. And his attention will be distracted by other things within his enlarged environment. So often, for these reasons, defective hearing is first noted at the toddling stage. Henceforth the child has to depend for speech acquisition on his own active interest. He must attract the adults' attention, he must ask, Why? What? Wherefore? When? How?—But the seeds of interest in speech, of interest in communication and his social gregarious interests have already been implanted.

Chapter 8

GESTURE AND THE DEAF

The association between speech and mental capacity has become recognized for so long that the word "dumb" has become synonymous with dull-witted.

FRY AND WHETNALL

SIGN LANGUAGES EXIST in many forms and in practically every part of the globe. Certain sign languages, appertaining to secret societies or religious orders, thrive in sophisticated complexity. The signs, so used, are not instantly recognizable or intelligible. They may possess a mystical symbolism regarded with reverence or with magical significance. The initiate is indoctrinated into their meanings or learns them by rote so that the sign can be used as a clandestine password permitting the cognizants to communicate in a manner that will not be recognized by others. These signs are jealously guarded and punishment will befall those who allow non-participants to learn their secrets. Other sign-languages, of which the signing of the deaf mute is the best known, depend on entirely opposite principles. Their meanings should be as easily and quickly apparent as possible, anyone should be able to learn and use the appropriate signs and supplement them with others which arise rationally or instinctively and are equally intelligible. These signs are *natural*.

In the course of time, even signs which were freely mimed take on a conventional appearance, but it is characteristic of natural sign languages that the number of "cryptogenic" symbols where the meaning and origin are not self-evident remains small and the number of natural or instinctive gestures which either mimic the specific appearance or function of the object concerned, or because they are so traditional or ingrained as to be obvious to peoples of every race and age are recognizable

95

and readily acceptable, remains large. With the more secretive languages, the reverse is true.

The sign language of the deaf is often regarded as not only natural but universal in that the majority of the conventional pantomimic signs which make up the language are mutually comprehensible to deaf people thoughout the world, and indeed can be widely understood by other users of natural sign languages— the North American Indian, the Australian aborigines and certain groups of Russian Armenians and Caucasians.

Herein should lie the secret of the genesis of signing and symbolism. But it is not so. The most primitive signers are in many ways the most complex in their signing, and their signs abound with a confusion of local variations amounting to separate codes. This is the situation among the Australian aborigines. The North American Indians possess a universal sign language to circumvent the difficulties arising from a profusion of local dialects and tongues; in many ways their manual signing constitutes a superior form of communication. Their environment and the terms they wish to use in their daily life differ markedly from the necessities of the deaf-mute existence, but as Mallory has reported (quoted by M. Critchley in *The Language of Gesture*) "the Indians can communicate without any difficulty with the deaf . . . there may be initial disagreement between the signs but they are mutually comprehensible, and signs of one system are often adopted by adherents of the other." Macdonald Critchley adds a further point, "The deaf mute enchances his gestures with lively facial movements, whereas the Indian's countenance remains grave and impassive. Perhaps too, the Indian's sign talk is less concerned with words than with ideas. Possibly also, the Indian's use of metaphore renders his sign-talk of higher esthetic worth than the others."

We should not become too excited over the so-called naturalness and universality of the sign languages, particularly if we are discussing them in relation to the deaf. There is much to be critical about. The present state of deaf signing is chaotic, partly because signing is not taught, partly because it is actively suppressed in schools and partly because educationalists refuse to learn even its rudiments. Mistakes are passed on, gestures are frequently copied incorrectly. Different institutions have their own conventional signs. Paget, who was as responsible as anyone for coining the expressions *natural* and *universal* when applied to the signing of the deaf, recognized many faults in their conventional signs. The signs, he considered, were unsystematic; there was no rhyme or reason behind many of them. There were too many local variants and confused meanings. The syntax was ungrammatical in comparison with the syntax of the English Language in which the deaf must read or write, or, if they can, speak. The habit of proceeding from the general to the particular is more reminiscent of French or Welsh syntax than English, thus they will sign "ball . . . red . . . Julie," or "Smith . . . letter . . . nothing," for "Julie's red ball" and "No, I have not received a letter from Mr. Smith."

Paget proceeded to produce his own systematic sign language. The Society for Deaf Welfare is preparing a less radical systematization of the existing conventional signs and the International Deaf Athletic Associations are combining to produce a mutually comprehensible sign language for deaf athletes of all countries.

The methods used by the deaf for communication are enveloped by strong emotional arguments. Educationalists concerned with the deaf usually hold that in all circumstances deaf children should be taught to speak before all else. Paget with his infatuation for gesture, provided an important, though scarcely less emotional, counterbalance. The oral method, dependent upon speech and speechreading (lipreading), was most favored in the past by schools for the deaf. This method is of mainly historical interest for it has been superseded by the aural method. Speech and lipreading are augmented, except for a few who possss no useful residual hearing, by the use of hearing aids. The aural method has taken over the whole ominous attached to the earlier oral method. It is most successful in those with a high IQ who begin speech training early in life and who have a reasonable degree of residual hearing. These children take to the use of a hearing aid far more readily than those who begin late. The late starters may fail to accept the hearing aid because their threshold for hearing approximates too closely to their pain threshold. As far as is known this is not a factor with the younger children and the distortion of noise from the set does not seem to trouble them. They use their auditory feedback to supplement their kinesthetic feedback and such visual aids as the teacher may provide. The success of the method depends upon good teaching, adequacy of intelligence and knack in the art of lipreading. Some children may even then find that their speech is unacceptable socially either because of imperfect phonation or because of embarrassing extraneous noises.

One stage lower in the hierarchy of deaf communication is finger spelling. This is done by the unimanual method in France and in the United States, and by the bimanual method in Great Britain. Historically it antedated speech training and experts may achieve considerable speed and grammatical accuracy by this method. Good finger spellers are often of high IQ. Many have started late in life and consequently have never acquired facility in lipreading. Finger spelling is a laborious form of silent communication: every word must be spelled out or shortened to recognizable abbreviations and each sentence consists of the letters of each word signed without gaps. The words are colourless, lifeless and without emphasis.

The use of conventional signs is frequently frowned upon by the older generation of finger spellers, by auralists and by teachers of the deaf. But the majority of deaf people prefer to augment finger spelling or lipreading by conventional signs and so add flavor to the conversation. The admixture of signs and finger spelling is known as the combined method.

Sign language unaugmented by fluent finger spelling may be the sole means of communication of those of low intelligence. This is a pitiful state of affairs. Chance becomes the master for the vast subject of signing is practically unchartered. It is not committed to textbooks and there are few other books available. It is not taught in the schools. It can only be picked up by haphazard means. Those of low intelligence who need to use it are unlikely to have received any formal training in its use. No one will show concern if the signs are unclear, and should any confusion or meaning arise it will remain uncorrected.

Once we have realized that four methods of communication are current among the deaf community, (1) *speech and speech-*

reading; (2) *finger spelling;* (3) *the combined method,* and (4) *signs only,* we can continue, without discussion of the ethics of each of these methods of instruction, to discuss the relevance of this hierarchy of communication among the deaf to the central theme of language. Let there be a pause for a moment of cynicism. Teachers of the first method may abhor gesture but frequently use gesture themselves either to indicate the position of the mouth in relation to a sound or to demonstrate the "feel" of the s and z sound properly made upon a hand held close to the lips Secondly, deaf children who fail to make progress with speech in their teens may be turned over by teachers dedicated to the oral method to others prepared to use combined methods. In certain schools, signs may be permitted outside the classroom but incorrect signs are never corrected. Finally, a schoolteacher may declare that all deaf children may be taught speech, little realizing that children with low intelligence or with multiple handicaps have been selectively excluded from his classes.

We may deduce from the foregoing discussion that we are unlikely to encounter a deaf person exhibiting the full potentialities of untrammeled gestural language. The brightest of those who habitually employ conventional signing will have combined it with other methods of communication. There are many thousands of conventional signs in existence but his vocabulary will almost certainly be small, prosaic and poorly signed. It may have been the medium of communication within his parents' home or his wife may have difficulty with speech. Having left school, he himself may have had difficulty in maintaining an adequate standard of speech and so taken to the combined method as a second resort. He may join a club and for the sake of companionship learn the combined method.

There is another difficulty in the realm of language. All deaf people, however they may have been taught, have difficulty in grasping concepts. Difficulties arise early in their education with regard to words like *on, before, after;* later on with such abstract words as *forgive, precisely, remainder,* and more importantly with the the teaching of morals, religion, sex, and the differences between personal and private property and wider world interests. Failure to understand concepts has been blamed upon both oral and manual teaching methods, but Pierre Gorman has rightly concluded that this is a universal difficulty for all deaf people.

Dr. Gorman showed me a copy of Charlotte Woolf's *A Psychology of Gesture* in which she writes that "it is only abstract thought which cannot be expressed in the language of gesture" and in a marginal note beside this statement Sir Richard Paget has commented in pencil that "abstract thought is expressible in gesture *exactly* as easily as in speech—viz by using concrete words (or signs) in a metaphorical way." If one already has a clear concept of what one means it is possible to express abstract thought in gesture. This is frequently done by Padres to the deaf in the course of their sermons; but it is doubtful whether an abstraction gestured in sequence by a series of people would be preserved in an intelligible form.

Signing, like speech, is an expression of a person's inner language and is therefore a higher cerebral function. In the chapter on the requirements for speech, the point was made that human speech differed neurologically from animal communication in that it could be abolished by a discrete unilateral lesion. The same is true of signing ability. Thus, J. Grasset in 1896 reported a deaf mute who lost his ability to make hand signs after a cerebro-vascular lesion. He tentatively concluded that there was a center for manual speech in the foot of the second frontal convolution of the left hemisphere. Tureen, Smolik and Tritt, in 1951, had a similar patient who developed apraxia and agnosia for dactylography and agraphia in the unparalyzed left hand following a hemorrhage into an infiltrating glioma involving the posterior portions of the left second and third frontal convolutions. There is some evidence that the center for finger spelling is distinct from that for signing: Macdonald Critchley (1938) had a patient, described as a partial deaf-mute who became profoundly deaf at the age of fourteen. He had never been proficient in the "natural" sign language and preferred lipreading or finger spelling. He lost the ability to finger spell but was still able to use his limited vocabulary of gestural signs.

There are valid reasons for treating these rare cases cautiously. These reasons are fully discussed in the original papers. Dactylographic apraxia or finger agnosia may have accounted for the earlier cases, while in that of Tureen psychological changes may have affected the presentation. Universal hand gestures are more primitive than finger spelling and as a shorthand method of expressing words and ideas by a single movement are more heavily weighted by affective qualities. No previous case has been recorded of the loss of this function in deaf mutes, although the possibility has long been anticipated. Any condition causing dementia will also disrupt the ability to sign. The patient may show a lowered intelligence, a limited attention span or a lability of mood which renders communication impossible.

The relationship of signing to lip movements in deaf communication is extremely difficult to understand. When a deaf person is signing, no sound may be voiced but he makes gross and exaggerated movements of his lips. Contrary to what one might expect it appears that the intelligibility of even the best signers is not enough, the face may be set in motion to indicate the underlying feelings, but there is no apparent reason why signs which are complete in themselves should require to be augmented by silent lip movements. These lip movements reflect the syntax of the signed communication and are quite different from the lip movements made when talking grammatically. Tervoort, in a study of the playground gestures used by deaf children in a Dutch oralist school found that manual communication was effective only when gestures were accompanied by mouthing of the spoken word on the part of the gesturer and lipreading on the part of the observer. When the lower part of the face was covered, the gestures produced by the child did not convey meaning to a second deaf child.

What exactly is contributed by the face is not clear. A deaf person who is speech-reading experiences a similar difficulty if the upper part of the face is covered. He can cope with a beard or a moustache but he has difficulty in reading a blind man, a person with a squint or a person wearing dark glasses.

It is quite possible that by watching the face, the deaf person achieves a rate of communication in excess of that achieved by the impassive Indians. A child may be capable of using a combination of natural sign language and lipreading so economically and rapidly that he may be capable of conversing with another child at about three times faster than spoken speech. In spite of this C. Fry has expressed his fear that the continued use of natural sign language may be detrimental to a child's ability to lipread. Most probably his fears rest on, the ungrammatical nature of signing and the absence of prepositions, definite and indefinite articles and tenses.

Rapid signing by the combination of hand and facial movements is extremely pliable. In the space of a few seconds, complex emotions, lipped words, spelled words, conventional signs and choreographic mime are stylishly incorporated into one delightful communication. "It is graceful and pleasing to the eye, and when an attractive facial mimicry accompanies the manual gestures, the result is eloquent indeed," A. H. Payne acclaimed it to be far more expressive, facile and beautiful than the English of Shakespeare and the Bible. Perhaps, Payne exaggerates, but no rhetoric is more prone to draw forth mass hysteria from the audience. It is characteristic of this manner of intercourse among the deaf that it is more intimate, frank and less restrained than that of the hearing world; the emotional pitch soon rises and the whole audience treats each topic with an intense, emotional and personal involvement.

Anthropologists will be tempted to draw a ready parallel with the rapid, emotional and incessant conversation of the longhouse. There are other similarities: the difficulty in indicating the tense, and in distinguishing between noun and verb—thus both the verb *to drive* and the noun *car* are indicated by a motion as if steering—and a lack of words possessing generic meanings, e.g., the words *to eat* are signed according to whether it means to eat ice-cream, fruit or meat, and *to wash*, according to whether one is washing one's hair, face, hands, feet, or clothes.

A definitive study has yet to be made of the processes whereby the deaf child acquires gestural language. With practically every deaf child an attempt is firstly made to train him to speak. Most schools and clinics strongly dissuade the parents from communicating to their child through signs. During the course of enquiries into the stages whereby a deaf child learns to express himself by gesture I have encountered three contrasting opinions: the first being that all children whether deaf or hearing possess a natural aptitude for gesture that is in excess of their aptitude for speech, that they are born mimics; another view admits to the existence of some spontaneous gesturing but this is dismissed as crude and ill-formed; and a third view holds that there is a noticeable lack of spontaneity of gesture among such infants—they can be taught to sign from an early age, but, as with an adult aphasiac they are incapable of initiation.

The first view receives most support in the literature but there is a definite suspicion for just this reason that it is founded upon armchair reflection. Sir Richard Paget has stated that the behaviour of the born deaf—who make emotional noises but possess no trace of speech—shows that speech is not an innate function and that pantomimic gesture is more natural than talk. H. Wallon, in *L'Enfant Turbulent,* makes a rather similar comment: "Expressive hand movements often precede verbal expression and correspond to a formative state of mental process. A creative effort can be traced in them." Curiously the people who most strongly support this view are school masters who are constantly faced with a flood of signing which they would prefer to suppress. Deaf children of school age are notoriously able mimics. Teachers recognize themselves or other members of the staff aptly portrayed, with amazing accuracy, by a few skillful hand movements. The more intelligent the child the greater their mimetic skill. But to say that this is true of the school child does not of necessity imply that the child under two starts life with all the natural endowments of a Charlie Chaplin, a Jacques Tatti or a Harpo Marx.

It seemed reasonable to suppose that some such inherent pantomimic skill might be expected early on in life from the more intelligent deaf children. This was my personal supposition until I questioned some of the small group of people who have tried to teach deaf children from the beginning in the precincts of the home. Those who have read the autobiography of Helen Keller will have realized what a vegetable existence she led until her helpmate Annie Sullivan forcibly inculcated an understanding of finger spelling for the deaf-blind. Helen Keller was not two years of age when she became blind and deaf and her early upbringing was psychologically disturbed. Annie Sullivan had to sow on barren ground, but by her singular perseverence she not only succeeded in teaching Helen Keller how to communicate, but instilled in her an energy and curiosity to learn more and more. The success story of Helen Keller, greater even than that of her predecessor, Laura Bridgmen, is the story of a determined and highly intelligent woman overcoming the dual handicaps of blindness and deafness in a remarkable way but the spark which set aflame this astonishing life had to be kindled and without this spark her intelligence would never have developed. The neglected child can develop an apparent dementia as gross as is found in any state of inborn oligophrenia.

The most graphic example I have personally encountered of this lack of spontaneity was in a family in which I questioned members of three generations. One of the brightest was a deaf mother of two normally hearing children. Her father was deaf and her mother had died in childbirth. She was brought up from five weeks until she was five years old by her aunt, who was the youngest and only non-deaf member of the previous generation. She taught her by signs and mouth-gestures from early infancy and later introduced finger spelling. It was her boast that when the child was eventually sent to a residential school for the deaf on reaching the age of five years she knew all the nursery rhymes and possessed a wide vocabulary. On further questioning the aunt could remember no attempt at spontaneous gesturing.

This example can be criticized for it was not obtained first-hand; but other examples can be cited at a similar remove. The pattern of behaviour which they show is not that which one would expect, if it is believed that children have an innate facility for gesture in advance of their facility for speech. There is much to commend the third proposition that spontaneous gestures exist but are crude and ill-formed; but the significance of this hypothesis still needs to be assessed.

Woolf's timetable for the development of gesture (*A Psychology of Gesture*) does not fit in with her initial statement that gesture is a preverbal language which starts at birth. She describes three types of gesture which govern the scene in infancy: automatic or reflex gesture; emotional gesture, and projective gesture—the terms are self-explanatory. Shethen describes a fourth type of gesture, that of imitation. At about two months the child may return a smile with a smile, at six months the child imitates gross movements using his arms and hands, and more definite imitative movements occur between eighteen and thirty months. But a hearing child will coo in response to a person talking to him at three months. At this time he is just beginning to move his hands toward his mouth. If at three months a parent makes vowel sounds, clearly and repeatedly, when the child is cooing the child will try to respond appropriately: one may distinguish between the responses to *i, ee, er,* and *ah.* By six months an English child will sound like an English child and unlike a German, Italian or Chinese child. By eighteen months he will also be using six to twenty recognizable words and echo others, i.e., at each stage vocalization appears to be in advance of gesture. This is true of the non-deaf child. There is no evidence to suggest that motor control, upon which gesture must necessarily depend, is hastened in any way if the child chances to be deaf, though often the vocal stages may be retarded sufficiently in these children to approximate closely to the corresponding stages of gesture.

If a child (it makes no difference whether he is hearing or deaf) is born of deaf parents and chances to move his arms in any way suggestive of an embryo gesture, the parents will applaud and encourage that gesture, especially if the situation is appropriate. This is identical to the manner whereby hearing parents will encourage and repeat back any syllabic utterance which appears to be meaningful. A hearing child in a non-vocal environment may realize before he is two that his parents are deaf and touch them rather than vocalize to obtain their attention. This is also true of a deaf child in a similar environment, but with a deaf child born of hearing parents there is apt to be an impasse in communication, especially if the parents are unaware that the child is deaf, neglect him because he is deaf (and often brood in guilt and self-reproach), or do not understand the elements of gestural communication. Such a child is liable to be backward in all communication and beset by psychological disturbances.

A deaf child will not derive the same satisfaction when gesturing to himself as a hearing child obtains through babbling. None of the stages of gesture correspond to babbling or to baby-talk; thus there is no tendency to reduplication of syllables e.g., *Ba . . ba . da . . da,* no equivalent to the childish endings, doggie etc., and no compulsion to be continually signing when playing by himself.

It may be said, in summary, that the deaf have several modes of communication open to them: which they choose depends more on social and educational pressures than on their own volition. The notion that deaf children gesture freely and spontaneously from an early age is probably not true. Once their interest is aroused they will tend to pick up conventional signs and the art of mime easier than finger spelling or speech. Literacy may readily be acquired by those who have learned finger spelling, but speech, vital for interpersonal communication in society at large, can only be acquired arduously.

All deaf people experience difficulty in mastering concepts. The student of language will note that defects of gesture can be producd by cortical lesions similar to those which cause agraphia, that though conventional signs are discrete in themselves concurrent lip movements appear to be necessary to render them easily intelligible, that word order when signing procedes from the general to the particular, that there are limitations in the presentation of verb tense, adverbs and certain generic terms, and that conversation among a group of deaf people frequently excites an intense personal involvement such as may be seen during conversation among aboriginal peoples.

Chapter 9

EXPRESSION, CONCEPT AND SPEECH

Human life as a whole is driven forward by its dim apprehension
of notions too general for its existing languages.

A. N. WHITEHEAD, *Adventures of Ideas*

THE WORD ANALYSIS has been applied to the classical concept of childhood speech. It has also been applied to the linguistic approach to language. The evolutionary approach has been used to describe the phylogenetic ascent of man. This gave way to the anthropomorphic approach when primitive races and early man became the primary subject of scrutiny. To describe the increasing specialization of the brain, the development of laterality and, in children, the steady growth of the child's spatial image the collective term organismic was found best suited to convey a complex series of discernable changes. The hypothesis of the active relationship of concept to speech can only be described as dynamic. It seeks in a unitary theorem to determine how and why speech arose and how and in what way speech and language are likely to change in the future. The first question is: What is a concept?

This question straightaway demands a change of course. It is not possible to define concept in purely receptive terms. Sensory reception, reflexes and any process of learning through repetition, conditioning or mimicry will not explain concept. We must break with the dependent, passive world of childhood and return to the likely eventualities wherein there was considerable pressure for the development of speech, the era when man, however primitive he may have been in those crude times, nevertheless responded to those pressures by the invention of language.

The word *conceive*, according to the Little Oxford Dictionary, has three meanings: to become pregnant, to form in the mind and to formulate in words. The first definition is irrelevant to our task, but the other two illustrate a duality which is hard to separate. The noun concept means an idea formed in the mind, an abstraction, a notion, a feeling, a thought, a mental consideration. These are all connected with the interpretation to form in the mind. A concept formulated into words is a concept given expression, hence the title of this chapter, "Expression, Concept and Speech." We may also deduce that there are concepts given expression (as in speech), and concepts without expression or yet to be expressed. As Galsworthy wrote, feelings often voiced cease to be feelings, feelings never voiced deepen with their dumbness. A concept, in another person, which remains unexpressed, we cannot know. A concept is known through its expression, be it action, writing, painting, music or speech. What then is the genesis of concept formation?

Theoretically, it may be stated that every newborn animal —child, monkey, crab or tadpole—learns instinctively to steer itself within its milieu. Every movement, a lion leaping, an eagle swooping, the flexion of an arm, can be envisaged as an act of navigation. To accomplish a planned action entails a cognizance of several factors. There must be awareness of the part to be moved as part of the whole body image and, beyond this, an awareness of the body's spatial orientation—the dimensions of the movement must be understood, for movement is a series of postures each with a new spatial orientation, and a new orientation of part to body. A movement takes time, for with the spatial change there is a temporal change; the smoothness of a movement depends on this factor. What the movement may achieve may depend on changes in the environment for which anticipatory adjustment has been made. This is probably not a complete factorial interpretation of movement but it is enough to suggest that any voluntary or purposive movement is a complex act of navigation (Sherrington). And yet, most movements we do in total unawareness of our performance—the movements are reflex or intuitive. It is not easy to determine where conscious action begins and reflex action ends. A lion hunting a young gazelle upwind would appear to be performing a more conscious act than a somnambulist or a person in a state of post-epileptic automatism.

In an earlier chapter a distinction was made between the crude sensation and the higher sensor perception of sensory stimuli received by a sensory end organ and transmitted to the brain. This is more than the chanelled filtering of afferent stimuli, selecting and modifying them in the process. There is an increasing integration, or blending, of sensory stimuli. In Sherrington's words (*Man on His Nature*) "the essential strategy in the evolution of the central nervous system has been not the elaboration of new venues of sense, but rather the development of increased liason among the existent major sensory imput systems."

The sensory areas of the cortex are interconnected, through thalamic connections and interthalamic nuclei, through callosal pathways joining the two cerebral hemispheres and through association areas adjacent to the primary cortical zones. In man, and more generally among the Hominoidea, there has been a notable increase in the bulk and extent of these integrating systems. Sensations are unconsciously received. For reflex action, conscious awareness is not required. But for all other actions, sensations must be fully perceived. The blending of sensory stimuli requires a scaled valuation of each sensation. The sensations become "indexed," that is to say they become represented quantitatively and qualitatively through the medium of "symbols"; thus sensation A may be equated with sensation B. A being knows of his own existence through the fact that during his waking hours he is continually made aware of himself through the bombardment of sensory stimuli. These amount to discomfort—awareness of an environmental situation in which he must partake; they seldom amount to actual pain. But just as a child's first cries are triggered by discomfort, so throughout life it is by discomfort that we are driven. The bombardment of sensory stimuli becomes built up and associated together to give that being a picture of itself within its environment. To define the word "perception" Gooddy and Reinhold (1961) used the phrase "the qualitative experience of a conscious person, evoked by or accompanied by . . . stimuli perceived as sensations which can be described in terms of symbols." It is not the quantitative but the qualitative focussing upon what is apprehended or understood which provides the perception, the mind's eye of a situation.

The formulation of a concept entails carrying over the symbols of perception into the process of thought. A concrete situation, seen and perceived, may evoke a thought-out response. Here the inner symbolism is derived directly from what has been

THE MECHANISM OF NON-INSTINCTIVE BEHAVIOR

STIMULI → PERCEPTION → { THOUGHT / MEMORY / ANTICIPATION } → EXPRESSION

perceived. Thought may also arise from stored perception or memory. Alternatively, a future situation may be "acted out" symbolically in the mind; its practicality assessed and, if later translated into action, the nature of that action is likely to be something more than would have been arrived at either reflexly or intuitively. Here again the symbols of perception are used to elaborate thought.

Do we know more about thought, or is what has so far been suggested mere surmise? We recognize visual thinkers who possess a visual memory and we recognize auditory thinkers with auditory memories; yet few people have purely visual or purely auditory memories. A person with a predominantly auditory memory thinks in words as though he were hearing them spoken. The possessor of a visual memory may be able to see and recall a whole page of print, a mass of written symbolism. People may suffer from hallucinations (these may be defined as sensory impressions in the absence of sensory stimuli), these hallucinations are frequently either visual or auditory—they hear voices and they dream.

Auditory symbols may thus be said to form part but not the whole of our conceptual thought. These symbols are used in the same way as nonlinguistic symbols. They can arise from the perception of crude sensations, they are organized into meaningful concepts and then they can be expressed. Anatomically the function of language depends on large areas of brain, overlapping and for the most part derived from the association areas. These are the repository of Hughling's Jackson's inner language. "Language," said Erdmann, "is not a kind of communication of ideas but a kind of thinking." Others have emphasized that external language is the symbolization of thought for the purpose of interpersonal communication, "a system of signs expressive of ideas (De Saussure), "a purely human and non-instinctive method of communicating ideas, emotions, and desires by means of a system of voluntarily produced symbols" (Sapir), and "a structure of signs, with the help of which the representation of ideas and facts may be effected, so that things not present, even things that are completely imperceptible to the senses, may be represented (Kainz).

It would be wrong to extrapolate that all inner language is necessarily composed of auditory symbols. Just as the vehicular basis of external language may vary—speech writing, printing, gesture, semaphore, morse code, etc.—so the vehicular basis of inner language may presumably vary. The person with a predominantly auditory memory may be better at understanding and speaking a foreign tongue than his friend with a visual memory, but this does not imply that he will cope better with a work written in a foreign language. Indeed, there is no proven correlation between linguistic ability and memory type. Wepman has emphasized that the nature of a child's conceptual ability once the child has mastered the written word. "Concepts," he declared, "are nurtured and developed through oral language, but are limited by the nature of the auditory modality upon which such language is based. As visual symbols become comprehensible and useful, however, no such limitations are necessary. The child as he acquires the ability to do his learning through the printed word also acquires the mechanism for greater abstraction. He is no longer bound to the temporal sequence of audition but develops the spatial sequences of vision." Here, quite possibly, lies the future line of development of man's mind.

For modern adult man, concept formation, symbolic thought and speech are inherently bound in the complexus of the mind.

They are superior to the "melody of impulses run off in the same settled manner" which subserve instinctive behavior. Thinking and speech are so interwoven that they appear to possess a common origin; but there is reason to believe that symbolic thought arose before speech.

To advane this point further we must pursue the same form of deductive reasoning which we have reserved hitherto for the discussion of speech in isolation, namely (1) to attempt to find concepts being used by animals other than man; (2) to follow the maturation of concept use in the individual up from infancy into adult life, and (3) to deduce the requirements and utilization of symbols in early man.

To attempt to find concepts being used by animals other than man is surely reminiscent of the time-honoured search for the origin of the soul—have animals souls; have animals the ability for symbolic thought? It is nonetheless a fruitful approach.

As children we quite possibly shaped a distinction in our own minds between the playfulness of the apes (loving the chimpanzees) and the playfulness of other animals. Perhaps the gorilla and the orangutan were too heavy for tricks and they were kept apart in their cages in ones and twos. The chimpanzees however, were a delight. The old ones could be as amusing as the young ones. We hooted with laughter. Part of the fun was derived from their doing things which were taboo to all of us, as for example hunting for fleas and other insects and then eating them. They exhibited an ano-genital license which shocked the adults. These were concrete acts related to their instinctive behaviour which like their appearance is almost human but not quite. The amusement we felt as they hung from the roof of their cages by their tails or used their tails in a prehensile manner also stemmed from their almost human propensities. We would never be able to do that feat. But they were also amusing because they played or acted in the true sense of the word, They would pretend to catch fleas and eat them. They would creep up on each other then scamper away. They would make rings catching on to each other's tails. They would play with objects as though the objects were animate. The keeper might scare them with a rag-doll or a piece of wood and they would cower away from it into a corner. They would deck themselves with hats, trying them on before a mirror and pulling faces as they did so. They would dance and parade. All these acts in fact possess a symbolic value which would not be the result of instinct alone. By contrast, the playfulness among other animals, as recognized by children, would be confined in the main to the behaviour of the young, the frisking of a levret a pair of lion cubs tussling with each other, a kitten chasing a piece of string. All these are instinctive acts in preparation for their future experience.

What we suspected as children has been shown more scientifically by comparative physiologists. Suzanne Langer believes that some objects—strictly limited in number and occurrence—possess a symbolic value and meaning for apes. (This view is supported by Kohler in *The Mentality of Apes.*) "If," says Suzanne Langer, "we take symbolic representation, rather than communication as the criterion of a creature's capacity for language, we see that the chimpanzee, at least, is in some measure prepared: he has a rudimentary capacity for it. Yet he definitely has no speech. He makes no stumbling attempts at words, as he does at using tools, decorating his body, dancing, and parading, and other primitive pursuits." Kluver, Bucy and others have designed experiments to show the possession of rudimentary concept usage by apes. For instance, if an ape is placed in a situation were he is unable to reach some fruit on a branch, he may succeed eventualy in knocking the fruit to the ground by means of a stick. The composite thought process, whereby he stops the direct attempt to reach the fruit and delays to pick up a stick before recommencing the attempt with the added advantage of a longer reach, represents Miller's flexible postponement.

Less readily, an ape may succeed in utilizing a stick which is not within his direct line of vision when faced with the task of reaching the fruit. Other apes may succeed in piling boxes on one another, usually somewhat precariously, in order to reach a tempting object. The most elaborate symbolic thought shown by animals is that which we admired as children, the chimpanzee playing with an inanimate object such as a doll as though the object were in fact animate.

The question of whether animals other than apes possess the ability of symbolic thought remains open. We can only suppose that if they have such an ability it would take a form not readily recognizable by our present methods of examination.

If we pass on to the second facet of the argument, we observe not surprisingly that a child's behaviour first manifests the use of concept when he begins to play actively, to exploit his surroundings constructively, to manipulate toys and so on. This sort of activity starts, according to Stein, between five and eight months and is firmly established by two years. Further evidence that the child is already building up concepts is seen in the use of gesture and the signalling of his wants by one-word sentences. More sophisticated evidence is revealed at about two and a half years, when the child begins to use shifters (I, you, my, mine, father, mother, home) correctly.

A remarkable illustration of the increasingly skillful use of concepts replacing cruder more primitive actions is provided by Watt's analysis of the maturation of quarrelling from crude fisticuffs to more discriminant disputation. He maintains that conversation, generally speaking, centers at first around disputes. "Quarrelling with words begins at about the age of five or five and a half, and, naturally perhaps, the countercheck quarrelsome and the reply churlish are learned before the retort courteous or the quip modest; indeed, the forms of speech used in polite disagreement are learned late, if at all."

Kinsbourne and Warrington showed that understanding of spatial discrimination of left and right—symbolic orientation— occurs between four and a half and seven and a half years, and Watts has shown that an understanding of generic terms (as is seen in primitive societies) is a late development, "If a child is asked in what way a penny, a nail and a knifeblade are the same, he is unlikely to say they are all made of metal before the mental age of eleven."

In the chapter on gesture and the deaf, we noted that the deaf experienced considerable difficulty and delay in learning the meanings of abstract words such as *remainder, precisely,* and *forgive;* ethical concepts and even relatively minor inter-personal mores were learned slowly and painfully, if at all. In the normally hearing child they would have been acquired as part of the child's awareness of his environment. Here we have evidence of the fusion of concept understanding and speech. Another example of this fusion arises from the mistakes of transposition of letters and syllables. Blau, in *The Master Hand* made a searching review of such mistakes and concluded that they were made by children learning to speak and again at the later stage of learning to spell and write.

Any discussion of the position of concept and speech in early man is an exercise of deductive reasoning. Facts we do not know. Presumably the concept of flexible postponement reached a higher peak in early man than it has ever done in the monkey world.

Homo fabricus, tool-making man, was obviously performing a task more difficult than that of an ape utilizing a stick. His habitat brought him into closer contact with other predatory animals such as bears who sought to occupy the same caves or mammoths whose tusks were useful for digging. A third factor making for greater complexity of life was man's diet. It will be recalled that baboons—monkeys that are mainly adapted to life on the ground—occasionally prey on lambs and other animals of similar size, using their powerful canine teeth as offensive weapons; and that this habit is liable to become more prevalent when conditions of existence are hard. Early man was principally a vegetarian but he was more ready to take to a carniverous diet than the baboons, and being without the dental and jaw structure of the baboons he had to use his hands as his principal offensive weapon. The way of life of early man—toolmaking, combative, and occasionally flesh eating—meant that he had to plan.

Often he had to plan an unseen battle, for example, to lure a woolly elephant into a trap. This trap could be comprised of a hollow covered with sticks and leaves. Once lured, they would wish to bludgeon the beast to death with stones and cut him up with clubs. How did he do it?

Man had to devise his scheme of attack beforehand with the

object of attack absent from sight and perhaps only anticipated. He had to envisage the contact of men and beast and forsee how best he can emerge the victor, and then he had to fashion his simple weapons accordingly.

From the fossil evidence of East Africa, Leakey and others have concluded that man first started fashioning tools and was certainly using eoliths, before he lost the simian grip, that is to say very early indeed, perhaps before pithecanthropus. Miller has further argued that the reasoning necessary in order that man will devise tools would not readily be performed without the power of speech. With the simplest tools, moreso perhaps than with the later more elaborated weapons, man had of necessity, if he were to have any expectation of success, to hunt as a pack. He had to coordinate with the others for the success of any ambush.

In the midst of battle, his hands would almost certainly be busied holding, throwing or swinging, so they would be useless for gestural communication. An additional consideration could well have been that any hunting expedition, particularly if it involved a trap or driving animals over a cliff-face, might well be carried out when the light was imperfect at dawn or dusk. Shouts of unseen savages might be highly effective as a means of terrorizing the beast.

We return to the old conundrum: Did early man first use speech or gesture? If he used speech, he would have been able to communicate in the heat of battle. He would most probably have called up the assistance of others by the empractic use of words and especially, as Diamond has suggested, of verbs—*break, cut, kill, lookout,* etc. In addition, he might have attracted the victim by imitation of the animal's call and later frightened it into a panic by a series of warlike shrieks. A more advanced man would introduce symbolic words by which to name or describe his victim: some would be imitative, others purely symbolic e.g., elephant. On the other hand if he had used gestures he would have had to plan and explain the whole exploit beforehand, introducing thereby a difficult temporal concept, he would nonetheless be unable to meet all eventualities. The gestures could not be confined to action words such as *break, cut, kill,* etc. they would have to include from the beginning a picturegram of the supposed victim i.e., nouns as well as verbs would be required to make even the most elementary sense. However, the symbolic status of a mimed representation of an elephant is infinitely more primitive than the word symbol elephant, great cow, tusky one, or whatever phonic description might have been used.

The conundrum remains. It would appear that the level of symbolization required for the application of gestural communication to the needs of primitive man balances almost exactly with the level of symbolization required for speech in the same eventuality. But there are reasons to suppose that speech might have had greater appeal to primitive man than gesture. The eye is a distractable sense organ; its attention can only be rivetted voluntarily. The ear cannot block out sound; listening is an involuntary act. One person trying to explain a project in vacuo cannot rely on the involvement of the others. He has to explain possibilities and probabilities, he has to be sure that what he says is absolutely understood for there will be other imponderables such as when the event may take place, or will the others remember what he has said. If he waits till the occurrence before gesturing his commands, he must firstly disengage himself from the combat and the others will have to watch his gestures whilst also keeping a wary eye on the enemy.

Speech	Gesture
Can be used at time of action.	Cannot be used at time of action.
Commander able to participate	Commander must have hands free.
Verbs necessary.	Object (noun) of action required.
	Time and place to be explained.
Can be used at night.	
Listeners hear involuntarily.	Sight is distractable.
Action provides emotional pressures for communication.	Reliance upon memory.
Noise often useful in battle.	Needs not immediate.

Such factors are removed if speech is the vehicle of communication. The rest of the tribe are emotionally involved from the start. The commander can lead them by example as well as by his shouts. The emotional pressures for communication which have formed the basis of so many theories of language are all present in these circumstances: the war-dance vocalization as part of emotion or muscular effort, the embroilment of the hands

so that other means of communication must be sought, and finally contact participation, the fears, danger, mutual assistance, rescue, kill, and joy of success.

Perhaps the most predominant fallacy found among speech theoreticians is that early speech can be equated with language stripped of everything save the essentials. This could never have been so. It would have suggested that primitive man had had a far higher intelligence than more modern man. Only a highly intelligent being could have invented Pidgin English, for example. In Jespersen's words: "If we consistently consider language as a set of human actions with a definite end in view, namely, the communication of thoughts and feelings, then it becomes easy to find tests by which to measure linguistic values, for from that point of view it is evident that that language ranks highest which goes farthest in the art of accomplishing much with little means, or, in other words, which is able to express the greatest amount of meaning with the simplest mechanism, and again, "The evolution of language shows a progressive tendency from inseparable irregular conglomerations to freely and regularly combinable short elements."

Far better not to regard early speech as essentially a vehicle for concepts; it had a hypnotic value. The exigencies of primitive life provided the prime impetus but in early discourse the few concepts present would have been almost certainly engulfed in a welter of irrelevancies. How many a leader of yore has set his crew laughing and forgot his course? The temptation to needless chatter has always been present. There has always been a hypnotic value in the sound of words, words for word's sake, word-spinning, the stirring of the emotions with meaningless chants, slogans, cliches or shouts. Doubtless people throughout the centuries, well into the mists of prehistory, have been hypnotized by the sound of their own voice and "misused the gift of the gab." This view is echoed by Malinowski who finds that among uncivilized peoples, speech scarcely serves as a vehicle of profound reflective thought. He dubbed this habit of platitudinous garrulousness "phatic communication." "Early man," wrote Malinowski, "like the modern savages, probably talked a lot but had little to say."

There are reasons why all this should be so. It is amazing how many quite intelligent people, even university students from different parts of the world, rely upon learning their text books by heart and subsequently fall down in application of that knowledge, because they have learned it is a meaningless and uncritical manner. Repetition is vital for such learning. A speaker addressing an unintelligent gathering, and, to a certain extent, any gathering, is often advised not to talk down to the audience, but equally not to be afraid of repeating himself. In the Army the NCO is never content to explain how a brengun works, the instruction must be repeated adnauseum until such knowledge becomes second nature. Repetition, too, is the basis of much subliminal advertising. Particularly in learning poetry the repetition of a phrase or its sonorous equivalent, the presence of a crude but rhythmic beat which can be incanted or to which the body can be rocked gently to and fro, aids the memory. Poetry is easier to remember than prose. Stilted, stylized, metre more easily remembered that the loose modern poetic idiom. The ancient required as many such mnemonic devices as possible to commit their sacred chants and sagas to the mind and it mattered not whether they were reproduced in a meaningful manner or as mystical incantations.

According to Langer, all forms of mystical incantation, most poetry, the use of repetitions, slogan calling to generate mass hysteria, and the babbling phase of infancy may all be termed generically "voice-play." By voice play a minimum of conceptual thought may be spread widely. It is the means for making the most of a limited ability, not so much on the part of the initiator, who almost always is superior to the listener, as to succeed in drumming into a simple mind an understanding or action, or even merely the ability to pass the information on unquestioning and without understanding to someone else who will eventually understand.

Evidence has accrued from the study of the burial sites of Neanderthal man that in the hegomony of this uncouth creature religious beliefs and a funery cult were already firmly implanted. Symbolic thought of a high and complex nature must, therefore, have antedated many of the tongues of the most primitive savages extant today. It is suggested that their beliefs were directed to a kind of polytheism of tree spirits and animal spirits as prevails today among pigmy tribes. But, when the Celts arrived in Britain they found megalithic monuments at Avebury, Stonehenge and elsewhere. These could have only been erected by possessors of a yet more abstract belief. The world of our predecessors was more complex than our own, more precarious, more ritualistic, and filled with all kinds of taboos and superstitions. The aboriginal of today is hedged about by similar rituals, taboos and superstitions. "The life of the savage is," to quote Jespersen, "regulated to the minutest details through ceremonies and conventialities to be observed on every and any occasion; he is restricted in what he may eat and drink and when and how; and all these, to our mind, irrational prescriptions and innumerable prohibitions have to be observed with the most scrupulous, nay religious, care; it is the same with all the meticulous rules of his language."

Primitive man, past and present, has overridden reliance on instinct which is the hallmark of the animal kingdom. He has been enabled to do so through his talent for symbolic thought;

but this same talent has only elevated him above the beasts, it has not set him free, it has merely rendered him subject to a new series of regulators, or governors of his existence, developed through and from symbolism. He has no fear of a stream, but in fulfillment of the aphorism "look before you leap" he must firstly placate the water spirit before he attempts to cross, thereby approaching the stream with caution. He should not kill recklessly or the animal spirits would ensure that he goes hungry in future. He must live in neurotic obedience to the sun or the moon or the stars. In his language, as in his religious ceremonies, he must do exactly right; he may have to say "beware" three times before he is understood or tap wood as he mentions a name. It is characteristic of the more illiterate regions of even quite civilized countries that unless a word is pronounced *exactly* right by a stranger they will fail to understand what is spoken. Not long ago—a point which well illustrates Jespersen's theory of the advancement of language through simplification—it was necessary to apply the correct collective noun in a host of circumstances: a sege of herons, a flight of doves, a claterynge of choughes, a muster of pacockys, a herde of cranys—to muddle any of these collective nouns would have resulted in total failure to be understood.

Early man moved from instinctive behaviour to one based on symbolic bewitchment. The lives of present-day men are largely controlled by jargon. To quote Bertram Russell (1921), *The Analysis of Mind*:

"Behaviourists say that the talk they have to listen to can be explained without supposing that people think. Where you might expect a chapter on 'thought processes' you come instead upon a chapter 'the Language of Habit.' It is humiliating to find how terribly adequate this hypothesis turns out to be."

In the scientific era we have carried the language of symbolic thought a stage further by the use of symbols of greater visual and auditory significance. Their understanding requires the full capacity of the intelligence. Whitehead warned us that the success of language in conveying information in the absence of a background of direct experience may be easily overrated. If a complex fact can be stated by means of a scientific equation, it is usually true to say that that equation represents the clearest and most concise form of presentation of that fact. The formula occupying one line may require pages of close print if it is to be transposed with full accuracy into word symbols. The neat, balanced formula, however, is more demanding on the specialized knowledge of the interpreter, though it presents in one accessible line a complete thought. Any carelessness or error is quickly seen and can readily be checked. One formula may be compared with another, added or subtracted. A formula may become the tool for further scientific work.

The advancement of any branch of science depends upon finding similar, clear, concise, thought symbols. Each form must be clearly understood and precisely used. A series of forms of similar precision may shape a thought or be "analyzed" or "digitalized" in a computer. In mathematics, in physics, in engineering and in chemistry the forms used may be letters, numerals or shapes used entirely symbolically. In the biological sciences and in psychology, there is less scope for the use of abstract symbols; their place is taken by words, often neologisms, and these words are defined with a precision of definition approximating that of the symbols used algebraically.

Abstract symbols or precisely defined neologisms form the language of thought within a specialty. All of us, to greater or lesser extent, learn a new language with every new subject we study: this language may be termed the jargon of the specialty. It follows that this jargon is important for it delineates our thinking in that specialty to an extent greater than we care to recognize. The jargon antedates us. If we apply it loosely we detract from its meaningfulness and our thinking becomes unclear. Only a few of us ever reach the position of being able to bend the jargon-structure of our specialty by adding to its vocabulary; and yet, we recognize that, though we cannot work effectively without precise definitions for the terms as we must apply them in practice, this jargon-structure, mostly built around definitions, mitigates against effective intercommunication between specialties. Those most coherent within their chosen specialty may be found quite incomprehensible when attempting to achieve a synthesis of thought between diverse specialties.

Remarkable lucidity in the use of plain words may be required to break through the barriers of specialty and interpret their complexities. A scientist is no artisan in the use of speech and language; he should be, and must be if he is to succeed, and experienced practitioner in their use.

Clarity of thought is an ideal to which we aspire. But we must not forget that all thought, however muddled and imprecise, possesses some germ of symbolism within it. On these terms it is possible to say that the ability for speech arose as a facet of the ability for symbolic or conceptual thought, and that the further clarification of this kind of thought provides a continuing impetus towards the simplification of our lives and the simplification of our language.

SUMMARY

My INTEREST IN the origin of language began as the result of a study of deaf children and hearing children with deaf parents. I felt that few books on language dealt adequately with the receptive aspect of language development. There were books on gesture and language, but few of these attempted an historical assessment of the importance of gesture to language. It is most improbable that gesture preceded speech, but kinesthetic sensation or "muscular memory" from the muscles of articulation may frequently underlie word selection and survival.

The language of primitive man was very probably ritualistic, conventional and muddled, much less meaningful than the hackneyed phrases and jargon with which we envelop our thoughts today. Clarity of thought, precision in speech and ability to state essentials—these are concepts to which we still aspire.

BIBLIOGRAPHY

ARIETI, S.: *American Handbook of Psychiatry*. New York, Basic Books, 1959.

BARBER, C. L.: *The Story of Language*. London, Pan Books, 1964.

BASTIAN, H. C.: Some problems in connexion with aphasia. *Lancet, i*:933; 1005; 1131; 1187, 1897.

BEATTY, R. T.: *Hearing in Man and Animals*. London, Bell, 1932.

BEERBOHM, M.: *Yet Again*. London, Heinemann, 1923.

BELL, P. R. (Editor): *Darwin's Biological Work*. New York, Wiley, 1964.

BLAU, A.: The master hand. *Res. Monogr.* No. 5. American Orthopsychiat. Ass. Inc., 1946.

BRAIN, W. R.: Speech and handedness. *Lancet, ii*:837-843, 1945.

————: *Speech Disorders*. London, Butterworths, 1961.

BREWER, D. W.: *Research Potentials in Voice Physiology*. New York, State Univ. of New York, 1964.

British Medical Journal: (Leading article) Noise and its effects. *ii*:605, 1965.

BURT, C.: *The Backward Child*. Univ. of London Press, 1946.

CAMPELL, O.: *"Mary Kingsley": A Victorian in the Jungle*. London, Butler, 1957.

CARRINGTON, R.: *A Million Years of Man*. London, Weidenfeld, 1963.

CASSIRER, E.: *Language and Myth*. New York, Dover, 1946.

————: *The Logic of the Humanities*. New Haven, Yale Univ. Press, 1961.

CIBA FOUNDATION SYMPOSIUM: *Disorders of Language*. London, Churchill, 1964.

CLARK, M. M.: *Left-handedness*. Univ. of London Press, 1957.

CLARK, W. E.; LE GROS, MEYER M.: Human cranium. *Brit. Med. Bull.*, 6:341-344, 1950.

CLARKE, A. M.; CLARKE, A. D. B.: *Mental Deficiency, the Changing Outlook*. London, Methuen., 1958.

CORFMAT, P. T.: Childless marriages. *Deaf Welfare*, 2:239-243, 1956.

CRITCHLEY, E. M. R.: Reading factors in a deaf environment. *Dev. Medicine and Child Neurol.* (to be published).

————: Hearing children of deaf parents. *J. Laryngol.* (to be published).

————: The social development of deaf children (Donald Paterson Essay 1966) *J. Laryngol.* (to be published).

CRITCHLEY, E. M. R., AND SECKER-WALKER, R. H.: A deaf-mute with Huntington's Chorea. *J. Neurol. Neurosurg. Psychiat.*, 29:181-183, 1966.

CRITCHLEY, MACDONALD: Aphasia in a partial deaf-mute. *Brain*, 61:167, 1938.

————: *The Language of Gesture.* London, Arnold, 1939.

————: The nature of animal communication and its relation to language in man. *J. Mt. Sinai Hosp., 28:*252, 1961.

————: Kinesics: gestural and mimic language. In *Problems of Dynamic Neurology.* Edited by L. Halpern, Jerusalem, 1963.

————: *The Parietal Lobes.* London, Arnold, 1953.

————: The origins of language. In *The Brain and Its Functions.* Oxford, Blackwell, 1957.

DANIEL, G.: *The Idea of Prehistory.* London, Pelican Book, 1962.

DARLINGTON, C. D.: The genetic component of language. *Heredity, i:*269, 1947.

————: *Darwin's Place in History.* Oxford, Blackwell, 1959.

DARWIN, C.: *The Descent of Man.* London, Murray, 1885.

————: *The Expression of the Emotions in Man and Animals.* London, Murray, 1872.

DAVIS, C.: Finger spelling and signing in the education of the deaf. *British Deaf News, 4:*10; 278-279, 1965.

DIAMOND, A. S.: *The History and Origin of Language.* London, Methuen, 1959.

DOBZHANSKY, T.: *Mankind Evolving.* New Haven, Yale Univ. Press, 1962.

DONOVAN, J.: The festal origin of human speech. *Mind, 16:*498-506 and *17:*325-339, 1891-2.

DOUGLASS, E., AND RICHARDSON, J. C.: Aphasia in a congenital deaf-mute. *Brain, 82:*68-80, 1959.

EISELEY, L.: *The Immense Journey.* London, Gollanz, 1958.

————: *Darwin's Century.* London, Gollanz, 1959.

————: *The Firmament of Time.* London, Gollanz, 1961.

EWING, A. W. G., AND EWING, I. R.: *Opportunity and the Deaf Child.* Univ. of London Press, 1947.

EWING, A. W. G., AND EWING, E. C.: *Teaching the Deaf Child to Talk.* Manchester Univ. Press, 1964.

FLETCHER, H.: *Speech and Hearing.* London, Macmillan, 1929.

FORDE, C. D.: *Habitat, Economy and Society.* London, Methuen, 1934.

GEORGE, W.: *Biologist-Philosopher—A Study of the Life of Alfred Russel Wallace.* London, Abelard, 1964.

GESELL, A.: *The Mental Growth of the Preschool Child.* New York, Macmillan, 1925.

————: *Infancy and Human Growth.* New York, Macmillan, 1929.

————: *The First Five Years of Life.* London, Methuen, 1940.

————: *Wolf Child and Human Child.* London, Scientific Book Club, 1942.

GIRSDANSKY, M.: *The Adventure of Language.* London, Allen and Unwin, 1963.

GOLDSTEIN, K.: *Language and Language Disturbances.* New York, Grune and Stratton, 1948.

GOODDY, W. W., AND REINHOLD, M.: Congenital dyslexia and asymmetry of cerebral function. *Brain, 84*:231-242, 1961.

GORMAN, P. P.: Certain social and psychological difficulties facing the deaf person in the English community. Ph.D. Thesis. Univ. of Cambridge, 1960.

GRASSET, J.: Aphasie de la main droite chez un sourd-muet. *Prog. Med., 4*:281, 1896.

HEAD, H.: *Aphasia and Kindred Disorders of Speech.* Cambridge Univ. Press, 1926.

HECAEN, H., AND ANGELERGUES, R.: *Left-handedness. Rev. Neurol., 106*: 510, 1962.

HOGBEN, L.: *The Mother Tongue.* London, Secker and Warburg, 1964.

HOLMAN, D.: *Noone of the Ulu.* London, Heinemann, 1958.

HOOTON, E. A.: *Up From The Ape.* New York, Macmillan, 1946.

ILLINGWORTH, R. S.: *The Development of the Infant and Young Child.* Edinburgh, Livingstone, 1960.

INGRAM, T. T. S.: Delayed development of speech with special reference to dyslexia. *Proc. Roy. Soc. Med., 56*:199-202, 1963.

IRVINE, W.: *Apes, Angels and Victorians.* London, Weidenfeld, 1955.

JACKSON, J. HUGHLINGS: Speech disorders. *Brain, i*:304, 1878.

JACOBS, N. J.: *Naming Day in Eden.* London, Gollanz, 1958.

JESPERSEN, O.: Language, Its Nature, Development and Origins. London, Allen and Unwin, 1922.

————: *Growth and Structure of the English Language.* Oxford, Blackwell, 1946.

JOHANNESSON, A.: The gestural origin of language. *Nature, 166*:60-61, 1950.

JONES, D.: *An Outline of English Phonetics.* Cambridge, Heffer, 1964.

KASTEIN, S., AND FOWLER, E. P.: Language development among survivors of premature birth. *A.M.A., Archives of Otolaryngology, 69*:131-1351, 1959.

KEITH, A.: *New Discoveries Relating to the Antiquity of Man.* London, Williams and Norgate, 1931.

————: *Darwin Revalued.* London, Watts, 1955.

KELLER, H.: *The Story of My Life.* London, Hodder and Stoughton, 1940.

KERRIDGE, P. M. T.: Hearing and speech in deaf children. *M.R.C. Special Report,* 1937, p. 221.

KLEIST, K.: *Sensory Aphasia and Amusia.* Oxford, Pergamon, 1962.

KOHLER, W.: *The Mentality of Apes.* London, Kegan Paul, 1925.

LAMBERT, W., AND FILLENBAUM, J. A.: A pilot study of aphasia among bilinguals. *Canada J. Psychol., 13*:28-34, 1959.

LANGER, S.: *Philosophy in the New Key.* Cambridge, Mass., 1942.

LEAKEY, L. S. B.: *Nature, 189*:649-650, 1961.

————: *Illustrated London News,* 238:346-348, 1961.

LENNEBERG, E. H., NICHOLS, I. A., AND ROSENBERGER, E. F.: In *Disorders of Communication.* Edited by D. McK. Rioch, Baltimore, Williams and Wilkins, 1964.

————: New directions in the study of language. *Mass. Institute of Technology,* pp. 65-88, 1964; also *Harvard Educ. Review,* 34:152-177, 1964.

LENNEBERG, E. H., REBELSKY, F. G., AND NICHOLAS, I. A.: The vocalisations of infants born to deaf and to hearing parents. *Human Development,* 8:23-37, 1965.

LEWIS, M. M.: *Infant Speech.* London, Kegan Paul, 1951.

————: *How Children Learn to Speak.* London, Harrap, 1957.

LILLY, J. C.: *Man and Dolphin.* London, Gollanz, 1962.

LUBBOCK, J.: *Origin of Civilization.* London, Longmans Green, 1889.

MARCHANT, J.: *A. R. Wallace: Letters and Reminiscences.* London, Cassalls, 1916.

McCARTHY, D. A.: *Language Development of the Preschool Child.* Minneapolis, Mennesota Univ. Press., 1927.

MILLER, G. A.: *Language and Communication.* London, McGraw Hill, 1957.

————: In *Disorders of Communication.* Edited by D. McK. Rioch, Baltimore, Williams and Wilkins, 1964.

MILLER, G. A.; GALANTER, E., AND PRIBAM, K. H.: *Plans and the Structure of Behaviour.* New York, Holt, 1960.

MORKOVIN, B. V., AND MOORE, L. M.: *Through the Barriers of Deafness.* New York, Macmillan, 1960.

MORLEY, M., COURT, D., MILLER, H., AND GARSIDE, R. F.: Delayed speech and developmental aphasia. *Lancet,* ii:463, 1955.

————: *The Development and Disorders of Speech in Childhood.* Edinburgh, Livingstone, 1957.

MULLER, M. F.: *Lectures on the Science of Language.* London, Longmans, 1891.

MURPHY, K.: Development of normal vocalisation and speech. *Clin. Develop. Med.,* 13:1963.

NEGUS, V. E.: *Comparative Anatomy of the Larynx.* London, Heinemann, 1949.

OSBORN, H. F.: Alfred Russel Wallace 1823-1913. *Popular Science Monthly,* Dec. 1913, pp. 523, 551.

OSGOOD, C. E., AND MIRION, M. S.: *Approaches to the Study of Aphasia.* Chicago, Univ. of Chicago, 1963.

PAGET, R. A. S.: *Human Speech.* London, Kegan Paul, 1930.

————: *This English.* London, Kegan Paul, 1935.

————: The origin of language. *Sci. News,* 20:82, 1951.

PARREL, S. DE.: *Speech Disorders.* Oxford, Pergamon Press, 1965.

PAYNE, A. H.: *King Silence.* London, Jarrolds, 1934.

PUMPHREY, R. J.: *The Origin of Language*. Liverpool Univ. Press, 1951.

REVESZ, G.: *The Origins and Prehistory of Language*. London, Longmans, 1956.

RIDDELL, F.: *The Silent World*. London, Blas, 1951.

RIOCH, D. McK., AND WEINSTEIN, E. A. (Editors): *Disorders of Communication*. Baltimore, Williams and Wilkins, 1964.

RUNDLE, S.: *Language as a Social and Political Factor in Europe*. London, Faber and Faber, 1944.

RUSSELL, B.: *The Analysis of Mind*. London, Allen and Unwin, 1921.

————: *Inquiry into Meaning and Truth*. London, Allen and Unwin, 1941.

SACIA, C. F.: Speech, power and energy. *Bell System Technical J.*, 1925.

SCHWIDETZKY, G.: *Do You Speak Chimpanzee?* London, Routledge, 1932.

SHERIDAN, M. D.: *The Child's Hearing for Speech*. London, Methuen, 1948.

————: The developmental progress of infants and young children. *Reports on Public Health and Medical Subjects 102*. London, H.M.S.O., 1960.

SHERRINGTON, C. S.: *Man on His Nature*. Oxford Univ. Press, 1929.

SINGH, J. A. L., AND ZINGG, R. M.: *Wolf Children and Feral Man*. London, Harper, 1939.

SMITH, G. ELLIOT: *The Evolution of Man*. Oxford Univ. Press, 1924.

SPIEGAL, R.: In *American Handbook of Psychiatry*. Edited by S. Arieti, New York, Basic Books, 1964.

STEIN, L.: *Speech and Voice, Their Evolution, Pathology and Therapy*. London, Methuen, 1942.

————: *The Infancy of Speech and the Speech of Infancy*. London, Methuen, 1949.

STERN, W.: *The Psychology of Early Childhood*. London, Allen and Unwin, 1927.

STEVENSON, E. A.: A study of the educational achievement of deaf children of deaf parents. *British Deaf News*, 4:10; 274-275, 1965.

SUTCLIFFE, T. H.: Conversation with the deaf. *Roy. Nat. Deaf Inst.*, 1964.

TAX, SOL: *Horizons of Anthropology*. London, Allen and Unwin, 1965.

TEMPLIN, M. L.: *Certain Language Skills in Children*. Minneapolis, Univ. Minnesota Press, 1957.

TERVOORT, B.: *Strurcturele Analyse van Visueel Taalgebruick Binnen een Groep Dove Kinderen*. Amsterdam, Noord Hollandsche, 1953.

TUREEN, L. T., SMOLIK, E. A., AND TRITT, J. H.: Aphasia in a deaf-mute. *Neurology*, i:237-244, 1951.

VILDOMEC, V.: *Multilingualism*. Basle, Sythoff, 1963.

WADA, J., AND RASMUSSEN, T.: Intracarotid injection of sodium amytal for the localisation of cerebral speech dominance. *J. Neurosurg.*, 17:266-282, 1960.

WALLACE, A. R.: The origin of human races. *Anthropological Review*, ii:158-

170, 1864.

————: *Darwinism*. London, Macmillan, 1889.

————: *Studies, Scientific and Social*. London, Macmillan, 1900.

WATTS, A. F.: *The Language and Mental Development of Children*. London, Harrap, 1944.

WEDDELL, G., FEINSTEIN, B., PRATTLE, R. E.: E.M.G. in the laryngeal muscles of man. *Brain*, 67:178, 1944.

WEPMAN, J. M.: *In Childhood Aphasia*. Edited by R. West, San Francisco, California Soc. for Crippled Children, 1962.

————: Dyslexia, language and concept formation. In *Reading Disability*. Edited by J. Money, Baltimore, Johns Hopkins Press, 1962.

WHETNALL, E., AND FRY, D. B.: *The Deaf Child*. London, Heinemann, 1964.

WHITEHEAD, A. N.: *Adventures of Ideas*. Cambridge Univ. Press, 1933.

WOOLF, C.: *A Psychology of Gesture*. London, Methuen, 1945.

YERKES, R. M., AND LEARNED, B. L.: *Chimpanzee Intelligence and Its Vocal Expressions*. Baltimore, Williams and Wilkins, 1925.

YERKES, R. M., AND YERKES, A.: *The Great Apes, A Study of Anthropoid Life*. New Haven, Yale Univ. Press, 1929.

NAME INDEX

A

Angelergues, R., 64, 127
Arieti, S., 125
Aristotle, 6

B

Barber, C., 72, 125
Barrington, Daines, 20
Bastian, H. C., 84, 89, 125
Beatty, R. T., 55, 56, 125
Beerbohm, M., 40, 125
Bell, P. R., 125
Bernstein, F., 44
Blau, A., 66, 69, 70, 115, 125
Boulle, P., 74
Brain, W. R. (Lord), 67, 70, 71, 125
Brewer, D. W., 125
Bridgman Laura, 104
Broca, 63, 64
Bucy, P., 113
Buffon, 5

C

Campbell, Olive, 14, 125
Carrington, R., 125
Carroll, Lewis, 26
Cassirer, E., 125
Chamberlain, H. D., 69
Chaplin, Charlie, 103
Charcot, J. M., 74
Cicero, 20, 26
Clark, M. M., 125
Clark, W. E. LeGros, 125
Clarke, A. D. B., 125
Clarke, A. M., 125
Corfmat, P. T., 125

Court, D., 128
Critchley, E., 102-4, 125
Critchley, Macdonald, 36, 96, 100, 125, 126

D

Dahlberg, G., 69
Daniel, C., 126
Darlington, C. D., 9, 53, 126
Darwin, C., 5-7, 9, 10, 19-21, 23, 27, 28, 30, 126
Davis, C., 126
Dax, M., 62
Descartes, 6
Diamond, A. S., 21, 29, 31, 47, 72, 116, 126
Dobzhansky, T., 126
Donovan, J., 17, 126
Douglass, E., 126

E

Edinger, E., 62
Eiseley, L., 9, 126
Emiliani, C., 61
Erasmus, 5
Erdmann, 111
Ewing, A. W. G., 82, 83, 126
Ewing, E. C., 126
Ewing, I. R., 126

F

Feinstein, B., 84, 130
Fillenbaum, J. A., 127
Fletcher, H., 126
Forde, C. D., 126
Fowler, E. P., 89, 127
Freeman, F. N., 69
Froment, J., 74

SUBJECT INDEX